A FISHERMAN CALLED SIMON

THE CALLED
BOOK 7

KENNETH A. WINTER

WildernessLessons

JOIN MY READERS' GROUP FOR UPDATES AND FUTURE RELEASES

Please join my Readers' Group so i can send you a free book, as well as updates and information about future releases, etc.

See the back of the book for details on how to sign up.

A Fisherman Called Simon

"The Called" – Book 7 (a series of novellas)

Published by:

Kenneth A. Winter

WildernessLessons, LLC

Richmond, Virginia

United States of America

kenwinter.org

wildernesslessons.com

Edited by Sheryl Martin Hash

Cover design by Scott Campbell Design

ISBN 978-1-9568661-1-7 (soft cover)

ISBN 978-1-9568661-2-4 (e-book)

ISBN 978-1-9568661-3-1 (large print)

Library of Congress Control Number: 2022918325

DEDICATION

To all those who have encouraged and challenged me through the years,
for your steadfastness in reflecting the grace of God to me.

~

My purpose in writing is to encourage you and assure you that the grace of God is
with you no matter what happens.
(1 Peter 5:12)

~

CONTENTS

FROM THE AUTHOR

A word of explanation for those of you who are new to my writing.

You will notice that whenever i use the pronoun "I" referring to myself, i have chosen to use a lowercase "i." This only applies to me personally (in the Preface). i do not impose my personal conviction on any of the characters in this book. It is not a typographical error. i know this is contrary to proper English grammar and accepted editorial style guides. i drive editors (and "spell check") crazy by doing this. But years ago, the Lord convicted me – personally – that in all things i must decrease and He must increase.

And as a way of continuing personal reminder, from that day forward, i have chosen to use a lowercase "i" whenever referring to myself. Because of the same conviction, i use a capital letter for any pronoun referring to God throughout the entire book. The style guide for the New Living Translation (NLT) does not share that conviction. However, you will see that i have intentionally made that slight revision and capitalized any pronoun referring to God in my quotations of Scripture from the NLT. If i have violated any style guides as a result, please accept my apology, but i must honor this conviction.

Lastly, regarding this matter – this is a <u>personal</u> conviction – and i share it only so you will understand why i have chosen to deviate from normal editorial practice. i am in no way suggesting or endeavoring to have anyone else subscribe to my conviction. Thanks for your understanding.

～

PREFACE

～

This fictional novella is the seventh book in the series titled, *The Called,* which is about ordinary people God called to use in extraordinary ways. As i've said before, we tend to elevate the people we read about in Scripture and place them on a pedestal far beyond our reach. We then tend to think, "Of course God used them. They had extraordinary strength or extraordinary faith. But God could never use an ordinary person like me."

But nothing could be further from the truth. The reality is that throughout history God has used the ordinary to accomplish the extraordinary – and He has empowered them through His Holy Spirit.

Simon was one of those people – and perhaps, for some of us, one of the most relatable. He repeatedly put his foot in his mouth. He often thought with his heart instead of his head. But he demonstrated that was not necessarily a bad thing. When he stepped out of the boat onto the water, he was thinking with his heart by faith; he got into trouble when he turned his eyes from Jesus and thought with his head instead of his heart. We, too, often find ourselves sinking in the circumstance that surrounds us when we make the same mistake.

Simon's life was a pattern of highs and lows. When he got it right, he REALLY got it right! For example, when Jesus asked the disciples who they said He was, it was Simon who boldly proclaimed, *"You are the Christ, the Son of the living God."*[(1)] But there were other times when he REALLY got it wrong! When Jesus was washing the apostles' feet the night before His betrayal, it was Simon who protested saying, *"No, You will never ever wash my feet!"*

In reality, Simon was the one who frequently had the courage to say what others were thinking but were afraid to say out loud. He was one of the most transparent disciples – if not, THE most transparent. He never did anything halfheartedly – he followed with his whole heart and jumped in with both feet. i don't know about you, but i want to follow Jesus like that! i want to be the one who is willing to go wherever He leads – without hesitation and not holding anything back.

It is clear through the Gospels that the sons of Zebedee – James and John – together with Simon had the closest relationship with Jesus. We could make a strong case that Simon was the closest of the three. i can't help but believe that closeness had a direct correlation to the depth of his love for Jesus. He was a great example of the truth: *"Draw near to God, and He will draw near to you."*[(3)] And i find myself praying, "Lord, give me that kind of love for You and closeness with You!"

By now, you are probably wondering why i continue to call him "Simon," and not the name Jesus gave him – "Peter." Simon was probably in his mid-to-upper thirties when Jesus gave him his new name. He was one of the oldest disciples, if not the oldest. As one who was in his mid-thirties when the Lord called me into full-time vocational ministry, i can relate to the changes in his life. And without question, the new name Jesus gave him signified the radical transformation the Lord brought about in his life. But for the purposes of this novella, i want us to remember that deep down he was Simon – an ordinary fisherman, husband, father, and brother – who got out of the boat and followed Jesus.

Simon was already a leader when Jesus chose him as one of His disciples. Some of those who also numbered among the twelve had previously been part of Simon's fishing crew. They already looked up to him and trusted him. And evidently the other men soon came to that same conclusion. Now before you say – "If that's the case, he wasn't ordinary, he was already extraordinary. I could never be a leader like Simon" – don't lose sight: God uses ordinary men and women with differing skills and abilities in extraordinary ways. Just think of Simon's brother, Andrew, whom God used to bring Simon to Him; or Edward Kimball, a Sunday School teacher, who led D.L. Moody to Christ; or a selfless Moabite daughter-in-law by the name of Ruth, who became the great-grandmother of a king.

God uses us regardless of our "skills." As a matter of fact, He often deliberately chooses to use those whom the world counts for nothing to bring about His extraordinary work.

i chose to write about Simon because i believe most of us only know him – or know about him – as a disciple of Jesus and an apostle. My desire is that you consider him as a person – a son, a husband, a father, and a brother. Since little is known about those parts of his life, you'll find that most of the fictional elements in this story are my attempt to paint a picture of what that may have looked like.

So, i invite you to sit back and enjoy this walk through the life of Simon and the other characters i believe are an important part of his story. You will recognize many names in the story from the pages of the Gospels and the Book of Acts. As in all my books, i have added background details that are not in Scripture, so we might see them as people and not just as names.

i have also added completely fictional characters to round out the narrative. They often represent people we know existed but are never provided details about, such as parents, spouses, or children. Included in the back of this book is a character listing to clarify the historical vs. fictional elements of each character.

Whenever i directly quote Scripture during the story, it is italicized. The Scripture references are also included as an appendix in the book. The remaining instances of dialogue related to individuals from Scripture that are not italicized are a part of the fictional story that helps advance the narrative.

i hope this book will prompt you to go to the Bible and read the biblical account of Simon's life. None of my books is intended to be a substitute for God's Word – rather, i hope they will lead you to spend time in His Word.

Finally, as i have already indicated, my prayer is you will see Simon through fresh eyes – and be challenged to live out *your* walk with the Lord with the same boldness, humility, and courage he displayed. And most importantly, i pray you will be challenged to be an "ordinary" follower with the willingness and faith to be used by God in extraordinary ways that will impact not only this generation, but also the generations to come . . . until our Lord returns!

~

1

THE SON OF A FISHERMAN

~

*T*he story goes that my grandfather, Avrom, was born on a boat in the middle of the Sea of Galilee. His fisherman father and expectant mother were crossing the sea when the baby surprised them by arriving early. My grandfather always told me he was a child of the sea from that day forward. He had his sea legs long before he learned to walk on land, and his first words were "Papa, fish!"

So it should come as no surprise that his son, Jonah (who would become my father), followed his father's lead and was weaned on the sea, always considering their boat to be his primary residence. Though his home was officially in the village of Bethsaida, spending time on land was something he did only when he had to!

Jonah grew up believing it was much safer to ride out a severe storm on the sea than it was on land. His reasoning? Because there were no trees to fall on you! Plus, it was a proven fact that homes built on land were sometimes submerged by flash floods. He much preferred to be on top of the water in his boat! The waves and the wind had never bothered him; they had been rocking him to sleep since he was an infant.

Fishermen are a tight-knit community with sea water flowing through our veins. We enjoy a common bond that land dwellers can't understand. Our shared love for the sea makes us more than friends – we are family, regardless of whether or not there is any blood relationship.

The biggest challenge for a fisherman is finding a wife who will understand her husband's love for the sea. More often than not, a woman like that is the daughter of a fisherman. The same can be said of families. There are basically two groups of people – fishing families . . . and those who are not!

As you would expect, my mother, Zivah, also came from a long line of fishermen – no pun intended! Though she was ten years younger than my father, both families had determined long ago that they would be married. Gratefully, my parents found the arrangement to be acceptable – though their approval was never a concern for their parents! My mother was fifteen when she was given in marriage to my father.

Since fishermen viewed their boats as their homes, they decided their places of lodging on land needed to house multiple generations. When my parents married, my mother simply moved from one house where her grandmother was matriarch to another where my father's grandmother was matriarch. The houses weren't far apart, and there was very little difference in size, shape, or way of life.

One year after their marriage, I was born. From the moment of my birth, there was little question that I favored my father – a fact that was only reinforced as time passed. I had his thick black hair, dark eyes, and rugged features. My father often told me that Jehovah God had made me perfectly to be a fisherman. As I grew, I was not only physically well suited for it, but I, too, loved the sea! Like my father, I believed that any day spent fishing was a good day!

Though fishing was our love, it was also the way we made a living and provided for our family. Some of our daily catch went to our family's table as well as the other families in the village; the remainder was our source of income – providing food for other villages and cities along the trade routes.

Each day we sold the majority of our catch to a man named Ishmael, who ran a fish-packing warehouse along the shore of the village of Capernaum. Though he had never fished a day in his life, he made a successful living by purchasing the daily catches from fishermen along the northern and eastern shores of the Sea of Galilee. He would salt and dry the fish to preserve it, then export each day's catch to other cities along the Via Maris – the trade route that connected Damascus with Egypt.

Over time, our Roman conquerors saw the growing profitability of the fishing trade and decided to take a greater portion of the income through increased taxes. Until that time, families had operated their fishing businesses independently. Despite my grandfather's initial misgivings, my father and his friend Zebedee quickly decided they would do much better working together than apart. Between them they had four boats which, if they joined forces, increased the likelihood of a consistent daily catch. The combined volume of their yield would also command a greater price from the fish-packing warehouse.

By the time I was fourteen, my grandfather and father decided I was ready to take over one of our boats. For the first few weeks, I was disheartened to find that my daily catch was always the least of the four boats. But my father kept assuring me, "Keep applying everything I have taught you, Simon, and soon you will be exceeding us all!"

He was right! Gradually I began to see my nets filled to the brim, and after a year, I was consistently bringing the second largest catch to shore – exceeded only by Zebedee.

As you can see, we worked hard each day. But to be more accurate, we worked hard for *six* days each week. On the seventh day, we observed the Sabbath. We gathered with our friends and neighbors in our synagogue in Bethsaida to worship God. And in obedience to His command, we observed the day of rest. Though I was not raised with an education beyond that of the sea, my heart was challenged each week by the reading of the Scriptures. To me, they were more than just words – they were life! But, at that point, I couldn't have told you why.

~

2

MY TEENAGE YEARS

~

On the eve of my fifteenth birthday, my paternal grandmother died. As the matriarch of our home, she had been responsible for holding our family together. Though all of us grieved her passing, I think my mother felt her loss the most.

In many respects, my mother had been closer to her mother-in-law than her own mother. Our culture was such that on the day of her marriage, my mother parted with her family and became a part of my father's family. It wasn't an intentional severing of family ties; rather, it was a product of the way the families functioned. So, with my grandmother's death, my mother lost her mentor and her closest female companion. It also meant my mother, at the age of 31, was thrust into the role of becoming our family's matriarch.

Following my birth, my mother had become pregnant three times, but all three of those babies had died in her womb. Slightly more than a year following my grandmother's death, my mother became pregnant again. We prayed this baby would survive and be born without any complication.

We also prayed for my mother's health. The loss of the three babies had taken a great toll on her, both physically and emotionally. Gratefully, my grandmother had been there at the time to comfort and support my mother. This time, however, if anything happened, things would be much different.

Thankfully, Jehovah God enabled her to carry the baby full term. When the day arrived, my grandfather, father, and I were out to sea as usual when my mother went into labor. She sent a message to her mother and sister, Huldah, to come help her.

When they arrived, they saw that my mother was in great distress. The closest physician lived in Capernaum. He would never arrive in time. So they sent word for the one midwife who lived in our village to come quickly. However, it became obvious the baby was ready to be born. The two women knew any delay would be dangerous for both mother and child.

As they later explained, my maternal grandmother and aunt assisted my mother during her delivery as best they could. Soon, both of them breathed a sigh of relief when my little brother was born.

"Zivah, he looks just like you!" my grandmother cooed. "He has your nose and your mouth. He is a beautiful baby boy!"

But my mother never heard those words. She had died giving one last push so her baby son could be born. She had taken her last breath one moment before he had taken his first.

Just then, the midwife arrived. She quickly surveyed the situation, and took over from my grandmother and my aunt. She cut the baby's cord and wrapped him in swaddling. She handed the baby to Aunt Huldah and went outside to find someone to carry a message to my father and me.

It was the sixth hour when we returned to shore and received the message. My father and I ran home quickly, leaving Zebedee and my grandfather to attend to our boats. By the time we arrived, my mother's body had already been prepared for burial. Our home was filled with women mourning her death. My father and I made our way to her bedside where my grand- mother and aunt were kneeling, my aunt still cradling my baby brother.

I had never seen my father cry . . . until that moment. And it wasn't a subtle cry – he wailed and wept with all of his being. If I had ever ques- tioned his love for my mother, that moment settled it. As much as my heart ached, I knew I needed to be strong to comfort him. To tell the truth, his reaction was more unsettling than the death of my mother.

Once my father regained control of his emotions, he took his baby son from my aunt and looked down into his eyes. But he immediately returned him to her.

"Huldah, I am a fisherman," my father said. "I have no idea what to do with a newborn baby. And when I look at him, all I see is my dead wife's face. Would you take care of him for me? At least while I grieve the loss of my wife?"

"What will you call him?" Aunt Huldah asked.

"His name is Andrew," my father replied, "because he will be bold and courageous like his mother."

My father and I took Andrew, when he was eight days old, to the syna- gogue for the rabbi to circumcise him. But after that, my father saw very little of Andrew for his first six years. After the period of mourning for my mother, he asked my aunt to continue to care for his young son.

"What does a house full of fishermen know about raising a baby?" he asked.

Each time I saw Andrew in the months that followed, he looked more and more like our mother – and I feared that would keep my father from bringing him home. But I knew he needed us . . . and we needed him. I continued to question my father, but all he would say was: "Soon."

One year after my mother died, my grandfather passed away. In addition to our grief and sorrow, we experienced a strain on our fishing enterprise due to grandfather's absence. My father compensated by putting even more effort into keeping our fishing boats running and "soon" continued to push out even further away.

∾

3

ANOTHER REASON TO VISIT CAPERNAUM

∼

a few years later, I was in Capernaum haggling with Ishmael over the price he was offering for that day's catch. Though we did not haggle every day, it was a fairly regular practice! Truth be told, I think we both enjoyed it!

In the midst of our conversation, we were joined by a fellow fisherman named Eber. He lived in Capernaum with his wife, Milcah, and their twin children, a girl and a boy. His son, Thomas, was in his mid-teens and worked on his father's boat. He was the next generation of a family that had been fishing these waters for many generations, just like our family.

Ishmael had announced he would be paying us less due to his increased costs to transport the salted fish to his customers. We all knew Ishmael was making more money on our fish than we were, so we were not going to sit by quietly and let this happen.

"Ishmael, our fathers have done business with you and your father, Shebna, since your fish-packing warehouse began," Eber told him. "We have always worked together to ensure we all get the best price possible. You offer us a service that Simon and I cannot provide for ourselves – and we, together with all of the other fishermen, provide the fresh fish that you are in business to sell.

"We cannot afford to reduce our price. We are already just scraping by. Simon and his father may be doing better than I am since they have four boats on the water, but I only have the one, and I can't possibly take anything less."

"We may have four boats on the sea, but that also means we split the money you pay us over a larger number of people," I interjected. "So this reduction in price affects all of us in the same way! Ishmael, you must be reasonable! Can you not increase the price to your customers to offset your increased transport cost?"

Our debate continued for quite a while – as it usually did – until we finally settled on a price. As Eber and I returned to our boats to unload our respective catches, we met his daughter who had just arrived with a sack of food for her father and brother. I don't believe I had ever seen her before – at least that I remembered!

"Simon, this is my daughter, Gabriella," he said as he introduced us. "And, Gabriella, this is my friend Simon. Together we just prevented Ishmael from taking advantage of all of us!"

I found myself interrupting him once more, saying, "Eber, I believe it was Jehovah God who intervened on our behalf!"

"Yes, of course!" he replied with a smile. "But by His grace, He chose to use us!"

Suddenly I realized I was staring at Gabriella . . . and at about the same time, so did the others. "Gabriella," Thomas joked, "he must be wondering if you have some food for him as well!"

She laughed nervously, as I awkwardly replied, "No, no. I have a sack of food on my boat. I must be going now. I need to get back to our boats and report the outcome of our negotiations to my father and Zebedee so we can unload our catch. They will be wondering what happened to me." As I walked away, I looked back and called out, "It was good to meet you, Gabriella!" as if she were the only one standing there.

From that day forward, whenever I was in Capernaum, I kept an eye out for Gabriella. My father and Zebedee quickly became aware of my interest and encouraged me to seek her out. Zebedee's wife was from Capernaum. He had met her several years ago when he found himself haggling with Ishmael. He had not been as successful with his negotiations regarding the price – but he ultimately ended up with a much greater prize – his future wife, Ishmael's daughter, Salome!

As it turned out, Salome and Gabriella's mother, Milcah, had been close friends since childhood. It was Salome who suggested to Gabriella's parents that they should consider me as a prospective suitor for their daughter. Gratefully, they heeded her suggestion, so as the months passed, I found myself spending more and more time in the village of Capernaum. I would often linger after selling the day's catch so Gabriella and I could spend the remainder of the day talking and walking along the shore.

One year after Eber introduced me to his daughter, I paid him the full amount we had agreed upon in our ketubah (marriage contract). Not long afterward, Gabriella came to live with me in Bethsaida as my wife.

With the return of a woman's touch to our home, my father soon warmed to the idea of having Andrew come live with us as well. Though our Aunt Huldah had been a wonderful caregiver, Andrew was overjoyed to be united with his family. Because of the age difference between him and me, he said it felt like he had two fathers instead of a father and a brother. And it was true, because father and I both kept a protective eye over Andrew!

As he grew, it became increasingly obvious that Andrew took after our mother, not only in appearance, but also in disposition, whereas I was more like our father. Andrew was soft-spoken with a gentle nature and much less animated than I was. Our father once joked that people ran from my high-spirited nature right into Andrew's approachable and welcoming arms. It was a fair comparison!

Even as a lad, Andrew brought the gift of song to our boats. We spent many an hour singing songs of praise to Jehovah God as we worked the nets. It wasn't the most melodious music you ever heard, but it was definitely the most heartfelt!

One day, as we arrived in Capernaum to sell our catch, we abruptly halted our enthusiastic singing when we saw a distraught Thomas along the shore. He had come to tell us his father had died while the two of them were on the sea fishing that morning. Eber's heart had apparently just stopped. I hurriedly returned to Bethsaida to tell Gabriella and bring her back to Capernaum so we could join her mother and brother in burying her father and mourning his loss.

$\sim$

4

SONS AND DAUGHTERS

~

*J*ust like my father, Zebedee has two sons: his oldest, James, is eight years younger than I am; and his youngest, John, is a year younger than Andrew. James and I both took after our fathers. We love the sea, we love to fish, and we are hard workers. As responsible eldest sons, we always knew we would be expected to take over our fathers' boats and continue the family fishing enterprise.

However, it was obvious early on that Andrew and John had other passions. Both had a desire to explore and learn about things other than the sea. They knew they needed to honor their fathers by working alongside them as fishermen, and they never shirked their responsibilities. But fishing wasn't their passion. To their credit, Zebedee and my father recognized the differences in their sons and attempted to encourage us all in the gifts and passions God had given us.

John, in particular, had a passion for studying the Scriptures. Periodically, Zebedee permitted him to take time away from the boat so he could sit under the teaching of Nicodemus, the rabbi in Capernaum. Zebedee even permitted John, after his bar mitzvah, to travel to Jerusalem on a couple of occasions to study at the school of Hillel the elder for a short while. Each time he returned home, we all benefited from what he had learned.

One year after Gabriella and I were married, Jehovah God blessed us with a daughter, Sarah, and three years later with a second daughter, Iscah. I am truly a blessed man. Both of my daughters take after their mother. They are beautiful – not only in appearance, but more importantly, they both possess the unfading beauty of a gentle and quiet spirit. My future sons-in-law will be blessed men.

I am grateful to God that my girls had the opportunity to know my father for a few years before he passed. Interestingly, my father was a more attentive grandfather than he had been a father. During his last years, he often told me, "After your mother died, there was very little reason for me to be home in Bethsaida. But my granddaughters have given me a reason to return."

We were pulling in the nets early one morning when my father dropped his rope and clutched his chest. He collapsed in the boat and drew his last breath. I called out to Zebedee to come help us. But there wasn't anything any of us could do.

That day I became the patriarch of our family and the new master of our family's fishing boats, as well as Zebedee's new partner. I will confess that stepping into that role was much different than I anticipated. It was one thing to have been a worker on the boat, but now I was the one in charge! That cloak of responsibility weighed heavily upon me.

I cannot begin to tell you how grateful I was for Zebedee. He had always been like an uncle to me, but now he became more like a surrogate father. He was the one to whom I turned for advice – particularly in my role as my brother's guardian.

Andrew was fourteen when our father died. Though he had always been respectful of me as his older brother, we both knew I was his brother – not his father. A teenager needs both! How was I to be the brother he needed but also fulfill the parental role he required? And I was also his "boss" – the one to whom he was accountable for his work on the boat. Zebedee gave me invaluable counsel on how to wisely juggle all of those roles.

When Andrew was seventeen, he and John approached Zebedee and me with a request.

"John and I have heard reports of a prophet named John the baptizer who is preaching a message of repentance and telling our people to prepare for the coming arrival of the Messiah," Andrew began. "All our lives, we have heard that the Messiah could come at any time, but this prophet is speaking of His coming with an urgency and an authority that exceeds that of anyone who has come before him."

"While I was in Jerusalem, all of the talmidim (students) discussed the Messianic prophecies with the rabbis each day," John added. "We began to hear reports about this baptizer, and we debated whether he was truly a messenger sent by Jehovah God. Since returning home, I have continued those discussions with Andrew, and our hearts are yearning to learn more."

"Simon and Zebedee, John and I would like to travel to the place along the Jordan River where the baptizer is preaching so we can hear him firsthand and see if the reports are true," Andrew continued. "We can then return and report back what we have discovered. We know it will leave you shorthanded on the boats, but would you consider allowing us to go? We will abide by whatever you decide."

"Allow Zebedee and me time to discuss it," I replied, "and we will give you our answer soon."

A few days later, Zebedee and I told them they could go. We, too, wanted to learn more about the message of the baptizer. Andrew and John would be our eyes and ears to report back everything they learned.

I had already been talking with Thomas about coming to work as a fisherman on our boats. Gabriella had confided to me that Thomas was not doing well operating his father's boat. He would do much better working with us. Plus, the steady income would better provide for Milcah.

Andrew mentioned that his friend Philip was also looking for work on a fishing boat. So, within a matter of days, we had hired Andrew and John's work replacements and released them to go.

I decided to sail the two of them across the Sea of Galilee to its southern shore. From there, it would be a three-day journey for them on foot to the place they had heard the baptizer was preaching.

5

ANDREW AND JOHN RETURN

~

*I*t was over two years before we saw Andrew and John again. One morning, as we were preparing to return to shore, we saw two men waving at us from the water's edge. It was James who first recognized them and called out, "It's John and Andrew!" Then he added half-jokingly, "The prodigals have returned!"

All of us were excited to see one another. After securing the boats and our nets, we made our way home. We had already sent word to Salome and Gabriella to let them know of Andrew and John's return. They prepared a feast!

After dinner, we gathered so we could hear their news.

"When John and I first spotted the baptizer," Andrew said, "he was standing on the west bank of the river in the middle of a large crowd. He was quite a sight! His clothes were woven from camel hair. His hair was disheveled. He spoke with a booming voice and his movements were even more animated than yours, Simon!" He stopped so everyone could enjoy a good laugh at my expense!

"But as we looked at the people in the crowd," he continued, "not one person was speaking or moving. He had their undivided attention as he shouted:

'Prepare the way for the Lord's coming!
Clear the road for Him!
I baptize with water those who repent of their sins and turn to God. But Someone is coming soon who is greater than I am – so much greater that I'm not worthy even to be His slave and carry His sandals. He will baptize you with the Holy Spirit and with fire.'[1]

"After he finished preaching, many in the crowd made their way to the water's edge and were baptized. As a matter of fact, before the day was over, John and I were baptized, too!

"We saw a handful of men who were the baptizer's disciples. He was teaching them from Scripture, and they were helping him minister to the increasing crowds. John and I quickly decided if we wanted to learn more about the baptizer and his message about the Messiah, we needed to become a part of that inner circle."

John then began telling us more of their story. "When we approached the baptizer about becoming two of his disciples, he stared at us silently with a gaze that seemed to penetrate our souls. Then he said, 'Our food is locusts and wild honey. Our bed is the ground we walk on, and our roof is the sky above us. If you have come out of idle curiosity, go home! But if Jehovah God has led you here, you are welcome to join us.'

"We became his newest disciples that day and continued to follow him for these past two years. We saw the growing number of religious leaders who came to satisfy their curiosity and suspicions about him. On many occasions, the religious leaders recognized me from my time with them at the school of Hillel. Seeing I was one of the baptizer's disciples, they would often come to me with questions about the prophet. The baptizer reminded me that most of the time, they were not seeking truth; rather, they were seeking to find fault."

"I, too, had many opportunities to speak with those who came," added Andrew. "Two were friends who had come together. One was a shepherd named Shimon, and the other was a zealot named Simon – though he looked nothing like you, brother!" he added with a laugh. "I could see that these men were sincerely seeking truth. They had many questions that I could not answer, so I introduced them to the baptizer. Soon, they, too, were baptized and became two more of his disciples.

"One day, John and I were standing with the baptizer when someone came walking toward us from the wilderness. We saw people arrive in large numbers each day, but they always traveled along the riverbank – either from the north or south. It was rare to see someone coming from the wilderness. So, this solitary figure caught our attention.

"As the Man drew closer, it became apparent He did not intend to join the crowd that had gathered. Rather, He continued to walk on by. As He did, the baptizer looked at Him and declared to no one in particular, *'Look! There is the Lamb of God!'*[2]

"John and I knew immediately that we were supposed to follow this Man. It was as if He had walked in this direction just so we would follow Him. And the baptizer's reaction to our hasty farewell confirmed that he also knew we were to follow this Man. We looked over our shoulders and saw that the shepherd Shimon was following along with us, as well.

"We had walked only a few steps when the One we were following turned around and looked at each one of us intently. It was as if He was looking into our souls. He asked us, 'What do you want?' Almost in unison we replied, *'Rabbi, where are You staying?'*[3] With an inviting smile, He answered, *'Come and see.'"*[4]

John picked up the story at this point. "It was four o'clock in the afternoon when we arrived at the place He was staying in Bethany. We remained with Him for the rest of the day.

"We learned that His name is Jesus of Nazareth. He began to teach us out of the writings of the prophets explaining what the Scriptures said. He spoke with an authority unlike anything we had ever heard. The hours passed quickly as He explained one truth after another. Our hearts felt strangely warm, and we knew He was the One about whom the prophets had written.

"As the hour drew late, we realized it was time for us to leave so He could rest. John and I knew we must return home to tell you what we had seen and heard. The Messiah has come! Jesus told us He would be traveling here soon and we would see Him again in a matter of days. So, three days ago, we departed in haste to tell you these things."

"We have met the Messiah!" Andrew exclaimed. "The baptizer declared Him to be the Lamb of God who takes away the sins of the world. We have sat with Him, and the Spirit of God has confirmed to us He is the promised One."

The room became silent as we all pondered what we had just heard.

∾

6

LET US WATCH AND SEE HOW GOD LEADS!

~

*W*e didn't have long to wait for Jesus to arrive. The next day, as we made our way to shore, Andrew spotted Him walking toward us along the shoreline. Andrew and John jumped out of the boat and ran toward Him, leaving the rest of us to follow once we had secured the vessels.

As I drew nearer, Andrew turned to Jesus and introduced me. He looked at me intently. I had never encountered a look quite like it. It was as if He was looking into my soul, with the knowledge of everything I had ever done – and everything I would ever do. I would come to believe that He looked at everyone not for who they were in the past, but rather for who and what they would become.

My assessment was quickly confirmed when He said, *"I will no longer call you Simon for you will be called Peter, which means 'a rock.'"*[1] He somehow saw me in a way that even I could not see. And for the first time in my life, I was struck speechless. I quietly stood there looking at Jesus while John introduced Zebedee and James to Him.

Next, Andrew introduced Philip to Jesus. Philip looked at Him with that disarming smile of his, which broadened even more when Jesus said to him, *"Come and follow Me."* [2] It appeared that Zebedee and I would need to hire another fisherman, because I could tell from Philip's expression that he would be joining Andrew and John in following Jesus. I decided I would seek out young Bartholomew and see if he was interested in working with us.

But apparently Bartholomew was on Andrew's mind, as well. He and Philip left to go into the village to search out their friend, who was also called Nathanael. He was originally from the village of Cana, but he was now living in Bethsaida. He was a practical joker and often found humor in even the most unusual situations. Andrew later told me when he and Philip told Bartholomew, "We *have found the very person Moses and the prophets wrote about! His name is Jesus, the son of Joseph from Nazareth,"* Bartholomew's immediate reply was, *"Can anything good come from Nazareth?"* [3]

That exchange was significant because when Andrew and John returned with Bartholomew, Jesus looked at him and said, *"Now here is a genuine son of Israel* – a man who says what he thinks." Bartholomew replied, *"How do You know about me?"* [4] Jesus explained that He had seen him standing under a fig tree before Philip and Andrew went to find him. Jesus had been nowhere near, and Andrew and Philip had not told Him they were going to find Bartholomew. But somehow Jesus had known. He had even known how Bartholomew would respond!

Immediately, Bartholomew exclaimed, *"Teacher, You are the Son of God – the King of Israel!"* [5] To which Jesus replied, *"Do you believe this simply because I told you I had seen you under the fig tree? You will all see much more than this! Come, follow Me."* [6]

It was then I realized Bartholomew would not be a possibility to replace Philip on the boat – I would need to find someone else. Jesus turned and smiled at me. He knew exactly what I was thinking.

Jesus told us He needed to go to Cana to attend a family wedding, and He invited us all to come with Him. We knew that Andrew, John, Philip, and Bartholomew would be going, but Zebedee and I needed to stay in Bethsaida to tend to our business. Gratefully, James and Thomas decided to remain and help us, because I was running out of men to enlist to replace those who were leaving to go with Jesus!

But those musings were overshadowed by more compelling thoughts about Jesus. I knew our lives would never again be the same. I was even feeling a tug at my own heart to leave everything and follow Him. But how could I possibly do that? I had responsibilities – to my wife, my family, and my business partner.

That night, I told Gabriella about meeting Jesus. I told her what He had said to me. "Gabriella, I believe He is the promised One," I said. "Though we only just met, I believe He knows me better than I know myself. I believe my life will be different because of Him. I believe all of our lives will be different because of Him!"

One of the greatest of God's blessings in my life is Gabriella. She is a wise, strong, and understanding woman. Those who know me will tell you I am an impulsive man with the tendency to act first and think later. Many times, I have come home discouraged by the events of the day, often the result of my own missteps. But my dear Gabriella would lovingly and patiently reason with me, caution me to go slowly, and encourage me to rise above my trials and disappointments. In sickness, she has been my comfort; and whenever I have followed my heart, she has been right there to cheer me on.

So I listened attentively to how she would respond to what I had just said about Jesus. She didn't hesitate. "Have you considered the possibility that you may be meant to travel with Him and become one of His disciples?" she asked. I couldn't believe she was asking me that question! I had been struggling with that very idea ever since the moment I met Jesus.

"I can't just leave and follow Him," I replied. "I can't abandon you and the girls, or Zebedee and the business. God has called me to be your husband, a father to Sarah and Iscah, and a partner to Zebedee. I cannot turn my back on you or what God has called me to do."

"You are a man of honor, Simon," Gabriella said. "That's one of the many reasons I love you. And I know you will never abandon me or your family. But I also know that if God calls you to follow the Messiah, you must do so. And we must all trust God to take care of us. His call on one of us is a call on all of us. If God so leads, the girls and I will go to Capernaum to live with my mother. We will be fine. I will trust God – and you must, also. Let us watch and see how God leads."

∾

7

AWED AND AMAZED

~

*I*t was the latter part of spring when Andrew, John, and our friends returned to Bethsaida. The daylight hours were approaching their longest of the year. The men had been away since autumn so they had a lot to tell us about Jesus and all they had seen Him do. But the first thing I noticed was the change that had taken place in each one of them.

The change manifested itself in subtle ways. It was apparent in the way they prayed. They had begun to thank God for everything they experienced throughout the day, and they referred to Jehovah God as the Father. They obviously were reflecting what they had seen and heard Jesus do.

Though John had always been more knowledgeable than any of us about the Scriptures, all the men now spoke with an understanding that far exceeded anything they had ever demonstrated. They talked about all they had seen Jesus do, not only with excitement, but also with awe and reverence.

They told us about how Jesus had quietly turned water into wine at a wedding celebration in Cana. "But His miracles didn't stop there," Andrew explained. "He healed the sick and the lame. He made the blind to see and the deaf to hear. We have witnessed Him cast out evil spirits from those who were possessed. And we repeatedly heard Him teach in the synagogue in a way that astounded even the rabbis."

"We followed Him to Jerusalem for the observance of the Passover," John told us. "When we arrived at the temple, Jesus did the unimaginable! He fashioned a whip from some ropes and proceeded to overturn the money changers' tables and drive the sellers and the animals out of the temple courtyard. Everyone watched in astonishment that anyone would act in such a bold way – including us. Even the religious leaders stood by silently without making any effort to stop Him. He chastised them for having turned His Father's house into a marketplace.

"It was at that moment I remembered the prophecy in the Scriptures, 'Passion for God's house burns within Me.'[1] And when the High Priest finally worked up the courage to confront Jesus and demand a sign to prove His authority, Jesus further astounded us all when He replied, 'Destroy this temple and in three days I will raise it up!'"[2]

Philip spoke up. "Because of His miraculous signs, many of the people in Judea are beginning to say He is indeed the Messiah!"

"Then on our return trip to Galilee, He unexpectedly led us to pass through Samaria," Bartholomew added. "We stopped at the well outside the village of Sychar to rest and get some food and water. He remained by the well while we went into the village to find food. When we returned, we were shocked to see Him speaking with a Samaritan woman. But from that single conversation, the people of the village thronged to see Him. They welcomed Him and as they heard Him speak, they believed in Him. Even the Samaritans came to believe He is the Messiah!"

We all sat there in amazement as we listened to their accounts. There was no question that Jesus was unlike any man we had ever known.

A few days later, we had been fishing all through the night but had no fish to show for it. We were washing and mending our nets the following morning when Jesus arrived on the shore. A group of people was following Him, and when the people of our village heard He was there, they came to see Him, too. Jesus began to preach to the growing crowd. Our fishing boats were there at the water's edge.

As the crowd pressed in, Jesus asked me if He could step into one of the boats and be pushed offshore a little ways so He could more easily address the crowd. I didn't hesitate and did exactly what Jesus asked. When He was done teaching, He turned to me and said, *"Now go out where it is deeper, and let down your nets to catch some fish."*[3]

"Master, we worked hard all night and didn't catch a thing," I replied. *"But at Your word, I'll let the nets down again."*[4] As soon as the nets were in the water, they began to fill with fish. I called out to Zebedee and the others to come out in the other boat and help Thomas and me bring in the catch. Soon both boats were so full of fish that we feared they would sink. I had never experienced anything like it!

Realizing what had just happened, I cried out to Jesus saying, *"Oh, Lord, please leave me, for I am a sinful man."*[5] Jesus looked at me and said, *"Do not fear! From now on you will be fishing for people!"*[6]

I looked up and saw Gabriella and our daughters in the crowd. She was smiling at me and nodding. We both knew what I must do. I turned and looked at Zebedee with a shrug that told him what I was thinking. To his credit, he also knew. James, John, Andrew, Thomas, Philip, Bartholomew, and I were all now preparing to leave and follow Jesus. Zebedee never once asked any of us to reconsider our decision. He knew Jesus's call on our lives to follow Him was also a call on his life to stay and maintain our business in order to provide the finances we would need.

I said farewell to my wife and daughters. Zebedee said goodbye to his sons – and to Salome, as well, since she had decided to come with us. Immediately we all departed with Jesus. I looked back once and saw my wife, my daughters, and my partner as they stood there watching us walk away. Without question, this was a journey that *all* of us were embarking on – and *none* of us had any idea where it would lead. Well . . . One did! And He was the One we were all following.

8

MIRACLES IN CAPERNAUM

~

*B*y the time we had made our way to the village of Capernaum, Gabriella and the girls had already moved there to stay with my mother-in-law. Though we had only been parted for a few days, it was good to be reunited with them. Since Jesus's mother, Mary, had also recently moved from Nazareth to Capernaum, Jesus told us He would frequent the village when He was in Galilee – particularly since the people in His hometown of Nazareth had recently rejected Him.

Salome's father, of course, still lived in Capernaum. She, James, and John were also grateful to be reunited with family, as was my brother-in-law, Thomas. So Capernaum offered good respite for us all.

The day after our arrival was the Sabbath, so we all went with Jesus to the synagogue. The chief rabbi, a man named Jairus, had grown up in Capernaum so several in our group knew him – particularly John. He and Jairus had both studied under the previous rabbi, Nicodemus.

When Jairus learned that Jesus was a respected teacher, the rabbi invited Him to read and teach from the writings of the prophet Isaiah. Jesus unrolled the scroll and found the place where this was written:

"The Spirit of the Lord is upon Me,
for He has anointed Me to bring Good News to the poor.
He has sent Me to proclaim that captives will be released,
that the blind will see,
that the oppressed will be set free,
and that the time of the Lord's favor has come."[1]

He rolled up the scroll, handed it back to Jairus, and sat down. Every eye in the synagogue was fixed on Him, waiting to see what He would say next. After a moment, He spoke these words: *"The Scripture you've just heard has been fulfilled this very day!"*[2]

He then proceeded to teach us many things about the One whose coming was prophesied by Isaiah. All who heard Him – including me – were amazed by His teaching and the authority with which He spoke. John constantly reminded me that Jesus had an understanding and recollection of the Scriptures that surpassed any teacher any of us had ever heard – including Hillel the elder. And the words He spoke were words of life, quite unlike those we had heard from our teachers of religious law. We wanted to hear more of Jesus's teachings. He assured us we would – another time.

Suddenly, a man possessed by a demon shouted, *"Go away! Why are You interfering with us, Jesus of Nazareth? Have You come to destroy us? I know who You are – the Holy One of God!"*[3]

But Jesus reprimanded him. *"Be quiet! Come out of the man!"*[4] He commanded. Immediately, the demon threw the man to the floor as those of us in the synagogue watched. Then it came out of him without hurting him any further.

Everyone was amazed, and many exclaimed, *"What authority and power this Man's words possess! Even evil spirits obey Him, and they flee at His command!"*[(5)] As you can imagine, the news about what Jesus had done quickly spread through the village. Jesus's words and actions were alive, and my spirit bore witness to the truth every time I heard Him speak.

After Jesus was done teaching, I noticed that my daughter, Sarah, had just arrived at the synagogue. She came to me straightaway with an urgent message regarding my mother-in-law. "Papa, Grandmother is very sick with a high fever. Mama asks that you come to Grandmother's home quickly . . . and bring Jesus!"

Rabbi Jairus joined us as we swiftly made our way to the nearby home. When we arrived, Gabriella pleaded with Jesus, *"Please heal her."*[(6)] He immediately made His way to Milcah's bedside and looked down on her with compassion. But then He spoke sternly – not to her but to the fever. He rebuked the fever, and immediately it was gone!

Within moments her temperature returned to normal. She sat up on her bed and looked at all of us standing around her. "I'm not sure what all the fuss is about," she said, "but it looks like I have a lot of company to prepare a meal for!" With that, she got up, joined Gabriella, and began to prepare a meal for her guests. It was as if she had never been sick!

In a matter of a few short hours, I had witnessed Jesus teaching in a way I had never known. I had seen Him cast out a demon in a way I had never seen. And now, I had seen Him heal my mother-in-law with a mere word. Surely, He is the Son of the Living God!

Word of Milcah's healing spread rapidly throughout the village, as well as those surrounding it. People began arriving in Capernaum to be healed by Jesus. Since the synagogue was the largest meeting space in the village, Jairus suggested Jesus meet with the people there. He greeted the continuing flood of people for the next several days – teaching the Scriptures and healing the people of their ailments and deformities.

Each day the crowd pressed in on Him – and many were forced to remain outside the synagogue and listen to Him through the windows. As the week progressed, a number of religious leaders from Judea arrived at the synagogue to investigate what they were hearing about Jesus. The crowd parted so the leaders could enter the synagogue, and there they stood against the wall looking critically at Jesus.

On the afternoon of the fourth day, I heard voices coming from the roof. A moment later, a small piece of thatch fell on my head. I looked up to see an opening in the roof above where Jesus was standing. I couldn't imagine what they were doing ... and apparently neither could anyone else ... except for Jesus!

9

AND THEN THERE WERE TWELVE

~

a pallet, with someone lying on it, was slowly lowered by ropes through the roof. At this point, even Jesus was looking up. Several of us realized the pallet was about to come down on our heads, so we quickly backed up to clear a space on the floor.

A young man lying on his back looked up at Jesus nervously, obviously not knowing what to say or do. Jesus looked down at him and smiled. He said, *"Young man, your sins are forgiven."*[(1)] Immediately, the religious leaders standing against the wall began to cackle like hens. *"Who does He think He is?"* they exclaimed. *"That's blasphemy! Only God can forgive sins!"*[(2)]

Jesus replied to them, *"Why do you question? Is it easier for Me to say, 'Your sins are forgiven,' or 'Stand up and walk'? So that you will know that I have authority to forgive sins, I now say to this man, stand up, pick up your mat, and go home!"*[(3)]

All eyes turned back toward the young man. The crowd gasped as he jumped to his feet. His friends on the roof began to jump up and down and cheer, "Glory to God!" For a moment, I thought they were going to fall through the roof! The religious leaders stopped grumbling and stared at Jesus in bewilderment. The young man stood there for a moment, unsure what he should do next. But then he bowed his knee before Jesus, looked into His eyes, and thanked Him. Next, he reached down, picked up his pallet, and walked out of the room. The people parted and marveled as they watched him pass.

By the time he got outside, the healed man's friends were already there to greet him. As they stood there together praising God, Shimon, the shepherd who was traveling with us, approached them. Shimon learned that the man had been paralyzed due to a fall from a rocky ledge the previous year. The young man was also a shepherd and had fallen as he was rescuing one of his sheep. Later that night, when Shimon relayed the young man's story to us, we all realized he had become one of the sheep healed and rescued by the Good Shepherd Himself.

As we departed from Capernaum the next day, we passed a tax collector sitting in his booth on the side of the road. He was stationed there to collect taxes from anyone bringing goods to sell in the village, as well as from anyone who had made a purchase and was taking goods out of the village. He appeared to be having a profitable day.

When we approached his booth, Jesus stopped directly in front of him, turned, and said, "Matthew, *follow Me and be My disciple!*"[4]

Thomas walked over to me and asked, "Doesn't Jesus know what this man does for a living? There isn't anyone lower than a tax collector! Why would Jesus invite him to be His follower?"

But he and most of those who were following Jesus were even more surprised when Matthew immediately got up, left everything, and joined Jesus. Out of the corner of my eye, I noticed the disdain on the face of one of the men who had joined us when we left Bethsaida. His name was Judas Iscariot, and I couldn't help but wonder what was causing his reaction. As if any of us were worthy to follow Jesus!

Jesus had now chosen twelve to be His apostles. There were the seven of us from Bethsaida – Andrew, James, John, Philip, Bartholomew, Thomas, and me. Two of our number were cousins of Jesus – the other James and his brother, Thaddeus – who were sons of a man named Clopas, the younger brother of Mary's husband, Joseph. They were already traveling with Jesus the day He had arrived on the shore at Bethsaida.

In addition, a man named Simon was already traveling with Him that day. But this Simon wasn't a fisherman like I was. In fact, he once numbered himself among the zealots. He and Shimon had apparently become friends in the zealot movement before they became disciples of John the baptizer. It was then that my brother, Andrew, met them. Simon had begun to follow Jesus about the same time as my brother and John.

Judas Iscariot just showed up one day. He evidently heard about Jesus and wanted to know more about Him. He was in the crowd the day Jesus spoke from my boat and had been following with us ever since. He seems to be a helpful sort who is always there to lend a hand. I'm not totally sure how genuine he is in his desire to help; he may just be trying to get on everyone's good side. Shimon told me last night that he also has reservations about the man, but I told him, "Jesus knows every one of us better than we know ourselves. And He appears to want Judas Iscariot to be one of His followers – so who are we to question Him!"

Matthew became the twelfth man. We are without question an unusual group: seven fishermen, two carpenters (not counting Jesus), one former zealot, one former tax collector, and I believe Iscariot was once a farmer. John is the most educated of all of us.

The group looks to me as their leader – after Jesus, that is. It has to do with what Jesus said the day I first met Him, the day He gave me a new name:

Peter, the rock. It's probably appropriate that a ragtag group of men should have a ragtag leader. But like I said before, Jesus chose us.

I don't know why He chose us. All I know is that He did. And I have decided to follow Him wherever He leads. Even if it leads to my death, I will never abandon Him.

～

10

I THOUGHT HE WAS SPEAKING
TO US

~

Several months later, we were back in Capernaum. The crowds Jesus was attracting were now so large He could no longer speak to them from inside the synagogue. Instead, we were meeting in large open spaces on hillsides or, as in the case of Capernaum, along the shore of the sea.

There were so many people crowding Him that we used Thomas's boat, sitting idle along the shore, so Jesus could be seated while He addressed the multitudes. We anchored the boat just offshore. It never ceased to amaze me the way He could teach for hours on end without a break.

And unlike the rabbis who often recited the law in ways that were difficult for most people to understand, Jesus used stories and parables that enabled everyone to better grasp the truth. For as long as I had been following Him, I could not remember Him ever telling the same story twice. He appeared to have an endless supply of parables with which to explain the truths of God.

He had begun soon after daybreak and continued nonstop until the sun was preparing to set. Finally, He told the people to make their way to their homes, and He told the twelve of us to get into the boat. The boat was similar in size to mine – about eight meters in length and two-and-a-half meters wide – so it could easily accommodate us. He told the women and the remainder of those who were traveling with us to remain there in Capernaum and await our return. Then He told the twelve of us, *"Let's cross to the other side of the lake."*[1] He directed us to the village of Gergesa on the eastern shore.

Jesus headed to the back of the boat and lay down for a well-deserved rest. We could tell He had fallen into a deep sleep even before we set sail.

An hour into our journey, a storm blew in without warning. Sudden squalls were common occurrences on the lake, particularly this time of year. The autumn winds tend to blow from the west, funneling between the hills and whipping the lake into a fury of waves. But that night, the winds and the waves were more severe than any I had ever seen. Massive waves were breaking over the boat, and we began to take on water. Despite our efforts at bailing water, we could not keep pace with the sea.

John looked at me as we were attempting to secure the sail and said, "This storm could sink us!"

I yelled to Thomas, "Go wake up Jesus and tell Him that we're about to sink in this storm. We need Him to help bail water!" Thomas made his way to Jesus, who was still soundly sleeping despite the howl of the wind and the violent rocking of the boat. He reached down and shook Jesus awake saying, *"Teacher, don't You care that we're going to drown?"*[2]

As Jesus opened His eyes, He looked at Thomas and then at the rest of us; He saw the fear written all over our faces. As He stood up, He looked at the waves crashing over the sides of the boat. Thomas was preparing to hand Jesus a bucket to help bail when suddenly, with a booming voice of authority, He said, *"Silence! Be still!"*[3]

At first, I thought He was speaking to us! I think everyone did. It never occurred to us He was speaking to the wind and the waves. But the wind immediately stopped, and the waves settled into a peaceful calm. I had never seen anything like it! I had seen Jesus heal the blind and the lame. I had even seen Him raise a young man from the dead. I had seen him fill my fishing nets to the point I thought they would burst. But in my wildest imagination I never thought He could command the elements of nature, and they would obey His voice!

The twelve of us looked at the sea and the horizon. We looked at the water rapidly escaping the boat deck through the side drains. Then we turned and looked at Jesus – our mouths gaping in awe and disbelief. Jesus looked at us and said, *"Why are you afraid? Have you been with Me all of this time, but still have no faith?"* [4]

I heard Bartholomew softly say what all of us were thinking: *"Who is this Man that even the wind and waves obey Him!"* [5]

Jesus lay back down and slept the rest of the way. I don't think any of us spoke a word until we arrived at the shore. We just continued to marvel at all we had witnessed – and who Jesus is.

My thoughts raced as I kept replaying in my mind what I had just seen. I ended up boiling it down to three important lessons. First, Jesus says what He means, and He means what He says. When He told us to get into the boat, He told us we were going to the other side. He knew we were going to encounter the storm. He always knows! And He knew that after He stilled the storm, we would arrive on the other side. He would always be true to His word, no matter what we might unexpectedly encounter.

Second, He was right there with us the whole time – sleeping peacefully, I might add. He was never anxious. He was always in control. And that would be true no matter what storm we experienced. He would always be with us and He would always be in ultimate control. We could trust Him and place our faith in Him.

Third, He has power over all things – illness, storms, even death – and we never truly understand any situation until we have heard from Him. Whether He said, "Man the buckets and bail the water!" or "Silence! Be still!" it wouldn't matter. I would trust Him whatever He said!

The sun was just beginning to rise as we approached the village of Gergesa. Off in the distance, I saw a man running toward the spot where we would soon come ashore.

~

11

HE CAME FOR THEM

⁓

*J*esus woke up just as we made shore. I wasn't really sure why Jesus had directed me to pilot the boat to this forsaken area. It had little vegetation and was surrounded by rocky hills speckled with caves that had been turned into tombs. In essence, this wasteland had become a burial ground.

Surely people from the nearby villages wouldn't come to this place to hear Jesus teach. Besides, to the best of my knowledge, no one knew He was coming that day, except possibly the man who was wildly waving his arms at us. As we drew closer, I could see he was naked. He was covered in dirt, his long hair was matted, and he looked like a wild animal.

Jesus stepped into the bow of the boat as if He were looking for something or someone. Instantly, the man began to shriek. Now, I knew Jesus feared no man, and I knew the One who had power over the wind and the storms – and even death – had power over everything and everyone. So, I knew He didn't need me to defend Him. But in my heart, I felt compelled to do so.

I walked forward in the boat and reached out my hand protectively to stop Jesus. "Please allow me to take care of this, Master," I said.

Jesus smiled at me with that smile I had come to know all too well. The one that said, "Peter, you don't really know what is happening here – but I do. Trust Me!"

Then He said something only I heard. "Peter, this man is the reason we sailed across the lake through a storm." I had walked with Jesus long enough to know He never did anything without a purpose. He never encountered anyone He didn't expect. But I still found myself wondering, "Jesus, what could You possibly have to do with this man?"

I lowered my hand from His shoulder, and Jesus stepped onto the shore. But I still followed right behind Him and stood at His side. James and John were immediately behind me. They, too, had similar thoughts about the need to defend Jesus. The rest of the men secured the boat.

As soon as Jesus's feet touched the shore, He said, "Come out of the man, you evil spirit."[1]

The man immediately fell to the ground and began to writhe in torment as he screamed, "Why are You bothering me, Jesus, Son of the Most High God? Please I beg You, don't torture me!"[2]

I looked at James and John. This man was obviously possessed by demons, who not only knew Jesus's name and who He was, but they were obviously afraid of Him.

Then Jesus demanded, "What is your name?"[3]

The demons replied, *"My name is Legion, because there are many of us inside this man."* [(4)] Then they begged Jesus not to send them into what they called "the bottomless pit." [(5)]

Not far away was a herd of two thousand pigs feeding on the hillside. *"Send us into those pigs,"* the demons begged. *"Let us enter them."* [(6)]

"All right, go!" [(7)] Jesus replied.

As I thought back on that moment, something became clear to me. The demons knew exactly who Jesus was and about His power and His mission. They knew the prophecies in Scripture that they would one day be judged by Him, and He would cast them into eternal damnation. They also knew the day of judgment had not yet come. So, when they asked to enter the pigs, they thought they were entering a safe place – at least for the time being.

But Jesus later explained that demons can no more see into the future than you or I. They only knew what God said through His prophets. So, when Jesus gave them permission to enter the pigs, they had no idea what was coming next! But He did!

That entire herd of pigs plunged into the lake and drowned – and those demons found themselves in the bottomless pit they had feared. They thought they could bargain with the Son of God but quickly learned they were ill-equipped to do so!

Apparently, the herdsmen ran into Gergesa and told everyone what had just happened to their herd of pigs. The people came running to see for themselves, and soon a crowd had gathered.

They saw Jesus sitting with the man, whose name we discovered was Enos. The villagers knew he was the crazed man possessed by demons. Yet here he sat fully clothed and perfectly calm! They couldn't understand what had transpired, and they became afraid. Soon they were pleading with Jesus to go away and leave them alone.

As Jesus began to make His way into the boat, Enos begged to go with Him. But Jesus looked at him and said, *"No, go home to your family, and tell them everything the Lord has done for you and how merciful He has been."*[8]

Jesus turned toward me and said, "And it's time for us to return to Capernaum."

Little did I know the people He planned to see upon our return. And little did a woman with a blood issue and a rabbi with a daughter who was about to die know that He was coming – just for them!

∾

12

A YOUNG BOY'S FAITH

~

*I*t was springtime and growing crowds were again following Jesus. One day, we were traveling through the hills, northwest of Bethsaida. As Jesus looked down at the throng of people assembled in the valley below, He had compassion on them and began teaching.

Late in the afternoon, I approached Jesus and said, "Master, *send the crowd away to the nearby villages and farms, so they can find food and lodging for the night. There is nothing to eat here in this remote place."*[1]

But He surprised me when He replied, *"That isn't necessary, you feed them."*[2]

Judas Iscariot had estimated the crowd to be about 5,000 men, plus women and children, for a total of approximately 15,000 people. Jesus turned to Philip and Judas who were standing beside me and asked, *"Where can we buy bread to feed all these people?"*[3]

Judas made it clear there was not enough money in the treasury to buy food. And even if there were, where could we possibly find that much food on such short notice? So Philip replied, *"We'd have to work for months to earn enough money to buy food for all these people!"* [(4)]

Jesus immediately responded, "Don't look at what you don't have. Look to see what the Father has already provided. *How much bread do you have? Go and find out."* [(5)]

Earlier in the day, a shepherd's son named Jonathan had climbed the hill to join Simon (the former zealot) and Shimon (the shepherd). The Spirit of God had recently restored the boy's hearing when the two men were visiting his village, and he had come to greet them. When he heard what Jesus said, the lad offered to give the food his mother had placed in his sack.

Andrew called to Jesus and said, *"There's a young boy here with five barley loaves and two fish. But what good is that with this huge crowd?"* [(6)]

Without any prompting, Jonathan walked over to Jesus and handed Him his small sack of food. Jesus gazed at the young boy so tenderly that, for a moment, it was as if time stopped. Jonathan's unselfish act made me realize he had more faith than all of us combined. This little boy wasn't concerned with how Jesus could use his small offering. He just knew he needed to give Jesus all he had.

Jesus looked at us and said, *"Truly, I say to you, unless you turn and become like children, you will never enter the Kingdom of heaven. Whoever humbles himself like this child is the greatest in the Kingdom of heaven."* [(7)]

With Jonathan remaining at His side, Jesus said to us, *"Tell everyone to sit down."* [(8)]

We directed the crowd to sit in groups of between fifty and one hundred. Then Jesus lifted the sack toward heaven and gave thanks to the Father for this young boy's faith. Next, He began to break the loaves into pieces, giving them to each of us to distribute.

We continued to serve the bread to the people until everyone had received enough. Then, Jesus did the same with the fish. He told us, after everyone had eaten their fill, *"Now gather the leftovers, so that nothing is wasted."*[9]

We filled twelve baskets to the brim with leftover bread and fish. As the twelve baskets were set side by side, I looked over at Jonathan. His smile extended from one ear to the other. I bowed my head and thanked the Father for what He had allowed us to witness that day. And then I asked Him to grant me faith the size of that little boy's.

The crowd had watched this miracle unfold. When they saw the twelve baskets, they exclaimed, *"Surely He is the Prophet we have been expecting!"*[10] They had come expecting Jesus to perform a miracle, and He had not disappointed them! The people began to clamor for Jesus to be their King, so they would never have to work for food again!

The increasing uproar made it clear the spectators were preparing to force Jesus to declare Himself as their King. He knew we were in danger of being caught up in the frenzy. Jesus took me aside and told me to take the disciples to my boat in Bethsaida and sail back to Capernaum. He then slipped away into the hills to be alone with the Father.

When we arrived at the boat, I decided to keep it onshore until Jesus joined us. However, when the crowd saw us waiting, they resolved to stay and wait for Jesus's arrival, too. After a while, I decided to take the boat farther from shore so the crowd would go home. There we would wait for Jesus to come back down from the hills.

But as darkness fell, I resigned myself to the fact that Jesus must have walked back to Capernaum and intended for us to go without Him. However, soon after we set sail for our twenty-minute voyage, a gale swept down on us, and the waves became extremely rough. I instructed the men to lower the sail and start rowing.

But it was of little use – we weren't making much headway against the wind and the waves. We had battled the storm for about five hours and were only halfway to our destination.

All of a sudden, one of the men called out that someone – or something – was walking toward us on the water. Thaddeus and his brother, James, cried out that it was a ghost. The closer the image came to the boat the more terrified we became.

Then we heard a voice proclaim, *"I am here! Don't be afraid!"*[11]

John looked at me and exclaimed, "Did you hear His voice? That's Jesus!" I could hardly believe it! I shouted, *"Lord, if it's really You, tell me to come to You, walking on the water."*[12]

Then, I heard my Master say, *"Yes, come!"*[13]

That was all I needed to hear! I jumped over the side of the boat and began to walk on the water toward Jesus! I had taken only a few steps when I turned my attention away from Him and set my eyes on the waves. As I did, I began to sink. I cried out in desperation, *"Save me, Lord!"*[14]

Immediately Jesus reached out, pulled me back on top of the water, and said, "Peter, *why did you doubt Me?"*[15]

He helped me back into the boat, and once we were both seated, the winds and the waves stopped. Jesus looked at each of us and said, *"You have so little faith.*[16] Believe, with a faith like that of the young boy you witnessed today!"

∼

13

THE SON OF THE LIVING GOD

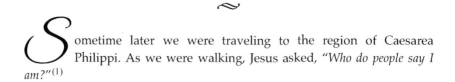

Sometime later we were traveling to the region of Caesarea Philippi. As we were walking, Jesus asked, *"Who do people say I am?"*[1]

The men responded, *"Some say John the baptizer, some say Elijah, others say You are one of the prophets."*[2]

"And who do you say I am?"[3] Jesus asked.

The men were surprisingly quiet. I'm not sure if they weren't quite sure what Jesus was asking – or if they were still wrestling with the question themselves.

But I did what I always do. I boldly proclaimed, *"You are the Messiah, the Son of the Living God!"*[4]

Jesus replied, "*You are blessed, Simon, son of Jonah, because My Father in heaven has revealed this to you. You did not learn this from any human being. Now I say to you that you are Peter (which means 'rock'), and upon this rock I will build My church, and all the powers of hell will not conquer it. And I will give you the keys of the Kingdom of Heaven. Whatever you forbid on earth will be forbidden in heaven, and whatever you permit on earth will be permitted in heaven.*"[5]

Then He sternly forbade us from telling anyone He was the Son of God.

As we continued our journey, we were uncharacteristically quiet as we pondered what Jesus said. We had known in our hearts who Jesus was . . . but He had just confirmed it!

When we arrived back in Capernaum, I was approached by a temple tax collector as I was walking through the village. "*Doesn't your Teacher pay the Temple tax?*"[6] he asked, accusingly.

The locals considered Capernaum Jesus's hometown since His mother now lived in the village, and it had become the center of His activities whenever He returned to Galilee. As a Jew, He was expected to pay the tax in His hometown. The temple tax was a law of God instituted through Moses,[7] which required an annual offering from each person twenty years of age and over for purification. Each person was to give half a shekel regardless of whether he was rich or poor. The offering was then used to care for the tabernacle and later the temple. I, like all other men, had been paying the tax since I had turned twenty.

I sensed the tax collector was attempting to accuse Jesus of violating the law. I hastily told him that Jesus would be paying the tax soon. I wanted to protect Him from yet another slanderous accusation by the religious leaders.

Later in the day, I approached Jesus about the tax. But He already knew what I was going to ask. I had come to realize that Jesus always knew what people planned to ask Him before they spoke.

Jesus explained an important truth to me that day about the notion of "purification." As Jews, we were to give the offering of purification in order to enter into the presence of a holy God. But as Jesus pointed out, He does not have to pay the temple tax because He is the Son of the King – and most definitely does not require purification. "For that matter," He said, "anyone who has placed his faith in the Son is a child of the King and is no longer required to pay the offering."

However, as the Son of Man, Jesus did not want to offend the people or have them think He was violating God's law. He had no reluctance challenging the traditions of men when they placed unfair burdens on the people. But this was the Father's law. Though He knew it did not apply to Him, Jesus also knew those around Him would not fully comprehend that truth – including me.

So, Jesus sent me to get the silver coin needed to pay the tax. But I was surprised when He told me where to go to get the coin!

"Go down to the lake and throw in a line," He said. *"Open the mouth of the first fish you catch, and you will find a coin. Take the coin and pay the tax for both of us."*(8)

He could have used anything to provide the silver coin. He could have directed me to get the coin from our moneybag. And yet, He chose a fish! I had been fishing all my life. I had harvested thousands of fish, and not one of them ever had a silver coin in its mouth! The whole idea was preposterous – and yet, after my experience of walking on the water, I was not about to question Jesus!

I recalled the day Jesus told me to *"Follow Him."* I had been fishing all night and hadn't caught a thing. But then Jesus told me to let down the nets into the deep water. And we caught so many fish the nets began to tear! So, I knew firsthand that Jesus had dominion over all of creation. If Jesus said the silver coin would be in the mouth of the fish – that's exactly where it would be!

The tax collector seemed surprised when I showed up with the coin later that afternoon. As I walked away, I heard him remark to the man who was standing with him, "It's easy to tell he's a fisherman. Even his coins smell like fish!" I thought to myself, "If you only knew!"

I often wondered how the Master orchestrated for that fish to have a coin in its mouth. And how He arranged for that particular fish to be the one I caught that day. I would never learn the details – and for that matter, the details weren't important. What I needed to know was that the Son of the Living God is always able to accomplish His purpose and His plan. And He accomplishes them through whatever means He chooses – whether it's a little boy's simple sack lunch or an unsuspecting fish!

~

14

OVERWHELMED!

~

*A*s extraordinary as my stories may sound, I assure you that everything I am telling you about Jesus is the absolute truth. I know I am a fisherman, but these are not clever "fish tales." Each thing I have told you about Him, I have witnessed firsthand. I *have seen His majestic splendor with my own eyes, and I have heard Him receive honor and glory from God the Father* with my own ears.[1]

By this point in my journey with Him, Jesus had twice called on James, John, and me to accompany Him while the others waited behind. The first time was the day we arrived back in Capernaum after He cast out the demons from Enos. Rabbi Jairus was waiting for Jesus at the shoreline. He had come to ask the Master to heal his critically ill daughter.

But while we were still on the beach, Jairus received word that his daughter had died. The messengers told Jairus, *"There's no use troubling the Teacher now."*[2]

Ignoring the messengers' comments, Jesus had turned to Jairus and said, *"Don't be afraid. Just trust Me."*[(3)]

Jesus sensed the disbelief of not only the messengers but also most of the crowd that surrounded Him, so He told them to wait there on the beach. Only He and Jairus would go see the little girl. I was surprised, however, when He turned to James, John, and me and told us to go with Him. He had never singled us out like that before.

When we arrived at Jairus's home, there was much weeping and wailing. As we walked inside, Jesus asked, *"Why all this commotion and weeping? The child isn't dead; she's only asleep."*[(4)]

Those gathered in the home did something that clearly showed they did not know who Jesus was – they laughed at Him. I had heard people laugh when Jesus told a funny story, but this was different. I had never heard anyone laugh at Him with such disrespect, ignorance, and faithlessness. I knew most of these people had not seen what I and the rest of the apostles had seen. But still, they had heard. The news of who Jesus was and the miracles He performed had traveled near and far.

When Jesus looked at them, their laughter subsided and turned into an uncomfortable silence. They had not learned to look at situations through eyes of faith. And to be honest, even with all I had seen, I was still learning myself. Because of their faithlessness, Jesus made them all leave the home.

Afterward, Jesus took Jairus and his wife, together with the three of us, into the room where the girl was lying. Then He took her hand in His, and said, *"Little girl, get up!"*[(5)]

Immediately, she sat up, stood, and began to walk around! To say the least, her parents were overwhelmed. I fell to my knees and prostrated myself on the floor. I was overcome with the feeling that I was too much of a sinner to be in the presence of Jesus. I recalled the words of the prophet Isaiah:

"My destruction is sealed, for I am a sinful man and a member of a sinful race. Yet I have seen the King, the Lord Almighty!" [(6)]

But instead of Jesus sending an angel with a burning coal to cleanse my lips, He reached down with His hand and gently lifted me up. "Peter," He said, "I have permitted you, James, and John to see this so you can bear witness after I am gone to what you have seen with your own eyes and heard with your own ears."

Jesus could not only heal the infirm, the blind, and the lame, He could also restore life to those who were dead. Though I had seen Him raise the widow's son from the dead, I had not been in a room with the boy's dead body beforehand. Somehow, being there in the room and observing the lifeless body of this little girl had felt even more real to me.

But some detractors said the little girl wasn't really dead; she was only asleep. I suggest they say that to those who initially laughed at Jesus, and hear what they have to say now. And as an eyewitness, I can testify that she was truly dead and came back to life!

The second occasion that James, John, and I accompanied Jesus was the day we climbed with Him to the top of Mount Tabor in lower Galilee. When we arrived, no one else was there. Jesus began to pray. As He did, His appearance started to change. His face began to shine like the sun and his clothing became dazzling white – far whiter than any earthly process could ever make it.

All at once, two men appeared before Him. Somehow, we knew they were Elijah and Moses. The two men were speaking of how Jesus was about to fulfill the Father's plan by dying in Jerusalem. I did not understand what they meant, but I was overwhelmed by the moment.

I blurted out, *"Master, this is wonderful! We will make three shrines — one for You, one for Moses, and one for Elijah!"*[7] My reaction clearly revealed my ignorance. Through my words, I had elevated the two prophets to being like God and unintentionally denied the deity of Jesus.

Immediately a cloud came over us and a voice called out from within it, *"This is My Son, my Chosen One. Listen to Him!"*[8]

James, John, and I were terrified! We fell face down on the ground. This time I was not only aware of my sinfulness and Jesus's holiness, but I was also acutely aware of His majesty and power. At that moment I feared Jesus . . . until I felt the touch of His hand.

He gently reached down to us saying, *"Get up. Don't be afraid."*[9]

He was standing there by Himself; Moses and Elijah had disappeared. Jesus told us it was time to go back down the mountain. As we did, He commanded us, *"Don't tell anyone what you have seen until I, the Son of Man, have been raised from the dead."*[10]

Though we kept what had happened to ourselves, the three of us often spoke of our fear and awe during the months that followed. Most of all, we asked one another what Jesus had meant when He said, ". . . until I have been raised from the dead."

∾

15

A FRIEND DIES

~

The two months following the Feast of Dedication in December are the coldest of the year. Because of the rain and cold, Jesus did not want to subject large masses of people to the elements. This meant He rarely traveled during those months, instead opting to stay longer in villages to teach small groups inside the local synagogues. Many in His 100-plus entourage even returned to their own homes during those months so they wouldn't be a burden on our hosts. So, we numbered about thirty during that time of year. For most of our third winter traveling with Him, we remained in Bethabara.

A messenger arrived from Bethany one day with a note for Jesus from his friends, Martha and Mary. His close friend – their brother, Lazarus – was seriously ill, and they believed he could be near death. The sisters' message simply said, *"Lord, Your dear friend is very sick."* [1]

Unfortunately, Lazarus died soon after the messenger left Bethany. By the time the missive reached Jesus, Lazarus's body was already being placed in a tomb.

When Jesus received the message, He told us, *"Lazarus's sickness will not end in death. It has happened for the glory of God so that the Son of God will receive glory from this."*[(2)]

We mistakenly assumed Lazarus was healed as Jesus spoke those words, just as others had been. The messenger would return to Bethany the next morning to find all was well with Lazarus – or so we thought.

Jesus, however, had a different plan. And though He loved Lazarus, Martha, and Mary, and did not want the sisters to experience the pain of grief, He decided to remain in Bethabara for two more days. We believed we were remaining there because Lazarus was already healed.

But on the morning of the third day after Lazarus's body had been placed in the tomb, Jesus announced, *"Let's go back to Judea."*[(3)]

Immediately I spoke up. "Rabbi, only a short while ago the religious leaders in Judea were trying to stone You. Surely, You don't want to go back there!"

Jesus looked at me and said, *"Our friend Lazarus has fallen asleep, but now I will go and wake him up."*[(4)]

"Lord, if he is sleeping, he will soon get better!"[(5)] Bartholomew told Him.

Bear in mind, we thought Jesus had already healed Lazarus until He clearly announced, *"Lazarus is dead. And for your sakes, I'm glad I wasn't there, for now you will really believe. Come, let's go see him."*[(6)]

Jesus's last statement shocked us. Lazarus was Jesus's friend. Why had He allowed Lazarus to become ill? Didn't Jesus's friends have special privileges over illness and the like? If Lazarus didn't have special benefits, what about us? Why had Jesus quietly waited two more days before announcing His plans to go to Bethany?

And why go back when we knew the religious leaders were plotting against Jesus? Why risk being killed to see a dead man? Why had He not just healed Lazarus from afar? He had done that before. We had seen Jesus restore life before, but those people had only been dead a short while. How long had Lazarus been dead? Wouldn't his body already have begun to decompose? Wasn't Jesus too late to do anything this time?

None of this made any sense to us. And why did He say, "For your sakes, I'm glad I wasn't there?" It was Thomas who ultimately said what we all were thinking, *"Let's go, too – and die with Jesus."*[(7)]

When we arrived in Bethany, the days of mourning were well underway. A large number of people were gathered at the home of Martha and Mary. Having been alerted that Jesus was nearby, Martha came outside the village to meet Him. But Mary remained in the house.

Martha's demeanor not only conveyed her grief but also her disappointment in Jesus. Though she knew Lazarus had died before Jesus received the message, she couldn't understand why He had waited so long to come see them. The messenger she sent to Jesus had already been back for two days. Also, Jesus seemed to know all things. Hadn't He known Lazarus was sick even before He received the message? He could have come and healed Lazarus while he was still alive.

Martha politely, but somewhat accusingly, said, *"Lord, if only You had been here, my brother would not have died. But even now I know that God will give You whatever You ask."*[(8)]

"Your brother will rise again,"[(9)] Jesus told her.

Martha, firmly believing the promise of Scripture that the dead will be resurrected at the last day, responded, *"Yes, he will rise when everyone else rises at the last day."* [(10)] But she did not believe – and in fairness to her, none of us believed – Lazarus would rise from the grave that very day!

Jesus told her, "Martha, *I am the resurrection and the life. Anyone who believes in Me will live, even after dying. Everyone who lives in Me and believes in Me will never ever die. Do you believe this, Martha?"* [(11)]

"Yes, Lord," she told Him. *"I have always believed You are the Messiah, the Son of God, the One who has come into the world from God."* [(12)]

Martha believed Jesus was the Messiah – and she had believed they would never die. But her brother *did* die, which was causing her to question the words of Jesus. Why had He permitted Lazarus to die? And what did that mean for the rest of us? She wasn't the only one struggling with the question – we all were!

∾

16

THE BEGINNING OF THE END

~

*W*hen Martha returned to the house, she told Mary to go outside and see Jesus.

The mourners at the house assumed she was going to Lazarus's grave to weep, so they followed her. When Mary got to Jesus, she cried out, *"Lord, if only You had been here, my brother would not have died."* [1]

When Jesus saw her weeping and the other people wailing with her, He became visibly troubled. I knew He was not angry with Martha and Mary. I didn't even think He was angry with the people who were sobbing with her. Several days later I asked Him to explain His reaction.

He told me the events were a harsh reminder of the ravages of sin and death upon His creation. He was angry with Satan for sowing the lies of fear and hopelessness. And He had wept over the fact that the One who is "the Resurrection and the Life" was standing there in the midst of us all, and none of us – Mary, Martha, the crowd, and not even those of us who were supposedly the closest to Him – had the faith to see Him for who He truly was. None of us believed He could raise Lazarus from the grave. The enemy had blinded us all with his lies.

As Jesus explained this to me, I felt like such a failure. The crowd at Mary and Martha's had simply mirrored the reactions of those of us who were His disciples. They mirrored our lack of faith. At a time when our words and actions should have helped build their faith, we led them astray from seeing Jesus for who He truly was.

"*Where have you put him?*"[2] Jesus asked those who had followed Mary. They told Him, "*Lord, come and see.*"[3]

When they arrived at the tomb, a stone was rolled across its entrance. "*Roll the stone aside,*"[4] Jesus told them.

Martha, who had also just arrived at the tomb, spoke up, protesting, "*Lord, he has been dead for four days. The smell will be terrible.*"[5]

Jesus responded, "*Didn't I tell you that you would see God's glory if you believe?*"[6]

So the stone was rolled aside. Jesus looked up to heaven and said, "*Father, thank You for hearing Me. I know that You always hear Me, but I said it out loud for the sake of all these people standing here, so that they will believe You sent Me.*"[7]

Then Jesus shouted, "*Lazarus, come out!*"[8]

The crowd was silent as all eyes focused on the entrance of the tomb. We could not imagine what was about to happen. I'm not sure if we stood there in faith believing Lazarus was about to walk out of the tomb, or in disbelief that Jesus would say something so outlandish. But I can tell you, no one looked away from the entrance!

Time stood still, then suddenly someone came hopping out of the tomb's entrance. His hands and feet were bound in grave clothes, preventing him from walking. His face was wrapped in a headcloth, so we weren't totally sure it was Lazarus. Jesus told those closest to him, *"Unwrap him and let him go!"*[9]

At first, no one moved. Was this a ghost? Would they be defiling themselves by touching whomever this was? Then one man stepped forward and began to unwrap the grave clothes. Soon another joined him, and then another. In a couple of minutes, they had unwrapped his arms and his legs and removed the head covering. There standing in front of us was Lazarus!

Martha ran toward her brother. Mary was conflicted whether to fall at Jesus's feet or run to her brother. She finally chose the latter. The crowd stood in stunned silence but then began shouting "Hosanna!" One by one, everyone turned and knelt at Jesus's feet. We knew we were on holy ground. As I knelt there, I saw movement out of the corner of my eye. It was Martha and Mary, together with the one who had been dead but was now alive. They, too, knelt to worship their Savior. Death had been defeated!

Yes, I had seen Jesus restore the life of the widow's son and Jairus's daughter, but I had not seen Him raise someone whose body had been in the grave for four days – and neither had anyone else.

Jesus taught us all many truths through that miracle. Three were especially significant to me. First, I learned the Master's timing is absolutely perfect. His delays are purposeful. He sees the big picture – and I don't. I must always trust His timing.

Second, Lazarus wasn't immune to death or disease as a follower – or as a dear friend – and neither am I. But I can be confident Jesus will always work everything, no matter what it is, in such a way that it brings glory to the Father.

Third, the only thing that stands between the spoken promise of God and my realization of that promise is my faith. I must guard against the enemy trying to limit my faith. Jesus is trustworthy. I can and must trust His Word. I can and must trust His promise. I can and must trust Him.

Many believed in Jesus that day, and His fame spread even more as a result. But some were fearful their way of life was about to change. They slipped off to the temple to tell the religious leaders what they had seen Jesus do. None of us knew it at the time, but in many ways the resurrection of Lazarus was the beginning of the end of Jesus's ministry on earth. Things would never again be the same.

~

17

WORSHIP AND ADORATION

~

Seven weeks later, we were back in Bethany at the home of Lazarus and his sisters. We were on our way to Jerusalem to celebrate the Passover, but Bethany was close enough that Jesus had chosen to lodge in their home. The sun had set, the Sabbath was over, and we were preparing to enjoy an evening meal.

Lazarus greeted his guest of honor with a kiss on the cheek. He anointed Jesus's head with sweet-smelling olive oil and provided Him with water to wash His feet. He pulled out his finest robe and placed it across Jesus's shoulders. Then he showed Him to the seat of honor at the table.

Lazarus invited the rest of us to make ourselves comfortable around the table. He positioned himself directly across from his guest so he could attend to any need Jesus might have. Jesus was his friend, and He was the Messiah. But to Lazarus, He was even more than that – He was the One who had power over death.

As we began to eat, Lazarus's sister Mary quietly came into the room. She approached Jesus from behind, carrying a beautiful alabaster jar. She knelt beside Jesus's feet and opened the jar. Suddenly the room was filled with the sweet, spicy, and musky aroma of an expensive perfume made from the essence of nard, considered to be the most precious of oils.

Initially, she poured a small portion of the oil over His head before she anointed His feet and wiped them with her hair. She was quietly expressing her love and thanksgiving to Jesus as the One who could conquer death. Jesus continued to eat and did not acknowledge her. The rest of us were silent. We just watched what was unfolding before our eyes.

Judas Iscariot broke the silence and said, *"That perfume was worth a year's wages. It should have been sold and the money given to the poor."*[1] A few of the other disciples followed his example, nodded in agreement, and began to scold Mary.

That's when Jesus spoke up and said, *"Leave her alone. Why would you criticize her for doing such a good thing to Me?"*[2]

A hush fell over the room as He continued. *"You will always have the poor among you, but you will not always have Me. She has poured this perfume on Me to prepare My body for burial. I tell you the truth, wherever the Good News is preached throughout the world, this woman's deed will be remembered and discussed."*[3]

None of us knew that in a matter of days, Jesus's body would be buried in a tomb. And here was Mary expressing her worship to her Lord in the best way she knew how, overflowing with love and adoration. I would think of that night many times in the weeks, months, and years to come. All of us sitting around the table that night would have said we loved Jesus, but all of us – save this one young woman – had an agenda. We all wanted something in return. Perhaps we wanted a position in His kingdom, or the power of His presence working though our lives, or His assurance of life and health. But this young woman had no ulterior motive. She simply chose to express her love in the purest way she knew how. This crusty fisherman had a lot to learn from her!

The next morning, we made our way toward Jerusalem. When we arrived at the Mount of Olives, Jesus called out to Andrew and Shimon, saying, *"Go into the village over there. As soon as you enter it, you will see a donkey tied there, with its colt beside it. Untie them and bring them to Me. If anyone asks what you are doing, just say, 'The Lord needs them,' and he will immediately let you take them."*[4]

I was surprised when Jesus sent them on their errand. He had never ridden a donkey the entire time I had been with Him. He had always walked. But though I questioned what He was planning to do, I didn't feel I could ask Him. He went to a secluded area of the mount to be alone and pray to the Father while we all waited for Andrew and Shimon to return.

When they arrived with the animals, they asked Jesus, "What should we do with them?"

"I will ride the colt alongside of its mother from here to the temple," He replied.

I was shocked once again. Why was He choosing to ride the colt? I was full of questions, but I kept them to myself. I knew Jesus would reveal the answers when it was time. Zechariah's prophecy never crossed my mind until much later:

Look, your King is coming to you. He is righteous and victorious, yet He is humble, riding on a donkey . . . riding on a donkey's colt.[5]

I placed my cloak over the colt to make it more comfortable for Jesus as He rode, and several of the other men did the same.

We began to make our way toward the Sheep Gate, the one Jesus most often used so He could quietly enter the city. However, Jesus redirected us. "Today we will enter the city through the Eastern Gate." Obviously we were not going to make a quiet, inconspicuous entry into the city this day!

As we continued on our journey, news spread quickly that Jesus was arriving. People poured out of the city to join the procession. Many began to spread their garments on the road ahead of Him. Others laid down palm branches they had cut in nearby fields.

A multitude soon surrounded Jesus so that He was in the center of the procession. Then spontaneously and continuously, the crowd sang and shouted with one voice, *"Praise God for the Son of David! Blessings on the One who comes in the name of the Lord! Praise God in highest heaven!"* [6]

The praises grew louder and louder as more people joined the procession. The entire city seemed to be in an uproar as Jesus entered. Some of the religious leaders even came out to see what all the commotion was about.

When they saw Jesus, they indignantly called out to Him, *"Teacher, rebuke Your followers for saying things like that!"* [7]

Jesus replied, *"If they kept quiet, the stones along the road would burst into cheers!"* [8]

The few who were unaware asked, *"Who is this?"* [9] The throng replied, almost in unison, *"It's Jesus, the prophet from Nazareth in Galilee."* [10]

When we arrived at the temple's entrance, Jesus dismounted the colt, and the mob of people parted so He could enter. The religious leaders watched Jesus closely as He walked through the temple. It was obvious the crowd's praise and accolades had agitated the leaders, but I had no idea of the plans they were formulating against our Lord.

Jesus chose not to teach the group assembling in the outer court that day. Instead, He motioned to us it was time to return to Bethany for the night.

Our trip out of the city was much quieter than our entry. The sun was beginning to set. It was going to be a beautiful spring night without a cloud in the sky. But unbeknownst to all but One of us, a storm was coming – and this time, Jesus had no plans to still it.

18

ONE SURPRISE AFTER ANOTHER

~

*T*he Passover Festival began at dusk on the fifth day of the week, starting with the Passover Seder (a ritual feast) and continuing for seven days. In preparation for the festival, all of the leaven was removed from Jewish households. Leaven symbolized corruption, or sin, so for the seven days of Passover we ate only unleavened bread. Any leaven remaining in the households on this day was removed and burned. That morning the pungent odor of burning leaven permeated the air in and around the city. Every household was busily getting ready.

The preparations were so important to Jesus that He sent John and me to make the arrangements. We all knew what was required under the law. And we had all traveled to Jerusalem many times for the observance of Passover. It would have been easy for John and me to do what was customary. But we had learned Jesus was always very specific in what He required of us, so I asked Him for instructions.

He told us, *"As soon as you enter Jerusalem, a man carrying a pitcher of water will meet you. Follow him. At the house he enters, say to the owner, 'The Teacher asks: Where is the guest room where I can eat the Passover meal with My disci-*

*ples?' He will take you upstairs to a large room that is already set up. That is
where you should prepare our meal.*"[1]

When John and I arrived in Jerusalem, we found everything exactly as
Jesus had said. The owner of the room, a tradesman by the name of
Yitzhak, not only provided the room free of charge, but he also provi-
sioned us with everything we needed for the Seder.

As was custom, the women traveling with us came along to prepare the
meal. Our followers now included Mary (Jesus's mother), Mary Magdalene (the woman from whom Jesus had cast out the unclean spirits),
Salome (Zebedee's wife), the other Mary (Jesus's aunt, Clopas's wife),
Joanna (the wife of Herod Antipas's royal attendant, Chuza), and Susanna
(the widow whose son Jesus raised from the dead). They busily began to
make everything ready for that evening.

Later in the day, Jesus and the rest of the disciples arrived. Before the meal
began, Jesus reclined at the table. Looking back, I cannot believe how calm
He was. Jesus knew what was about to unfold; and yet, there He was
looking completely relaxed. I would have at least been anxious, if not
outright panicked. But, as the Son of God, He knew that everything was
going to happen according to His Father's plan. So, He rested and
renewed His strength for what was coming.

Jesus knew the very foundation of our belief in Him was about to be
shaken. He was aware of the tragedy and despair we would experience.
He began pouring into us, nurturing us, and encouraging us one last time
before those things happened. He knew exactly what we needed. But He
also knew the victory we would witness and experience on the other side
of our pain. He made every minute with us count, preparing us to walk
through the hours ahead.

Then Jesus did something that astonished me. He got up from the table
and kneeled before each one of us and washed our dirty feet. He then
dried them with the towel He wore around His waist.

I watched with horror! The Son of the Almighty God was washing our feet! I looked around the room at His disciples: a group of fishermen, carpenters, zealots, and tax collectors. All of us were sinners, and none of us deserved His grace – let alone having Him wash our feet. This was our Lord and our Master serving us in such a humble way. A silence fell over the room as Jesus knelt before one man and then the next.

When Jesus came to me, I could not sit by silently and allow Him to do this. I protested saying, *"Lord, are You going to wash my feet?"*[2]

Jesus looked at me and patiently replied, *"You don't understand now what I am doing, but someday you will."*[3]

"No," I protested again, *"You will never ever wash my feet!"*[4]

"Unless I wash you, you won't belong to Me,"[5] He said.

"I won't belong to Him!" I thought. "That can never be!" Then in my typical bombastic way, I exclaimed in resignation, *"Then wash my hands and head as well, Lord, not just my feet!"*[6]

My Lord responded, *"A person who has bathed all over does not need to wash, except for the feet, to be entirely clean. And you disciples are clean, but not all of you."*[7]

I was curious what Jesus meant by those last few words. But before the sun rose again, I would be painfully aware.

When Jesus finished washing everyone's feet, He put His robe back on and returned to His place at the table. *"Do you understand what I was doing?"* He asked. *"You call Me 'Teacher' and 'Lord,' and you are right, because that's what I* am. And since I, your Lord and Teacher, have washed your feet, you ought to wash each other's feet. I have given you an example to follow. Do as I have done to you. I tell you the truth, slaves are not greater than their master. Nor is the messenger more important than the One who sends the message. Now that you know these things, God will bless you for doing them."[8]

As we ate the Passover meal, I thought about what Jesus had just said and done. But my thoughts were interrupted when He spoke these words: "Here at this table, sitting among us as a friend, is the man who will betray Me. For it has been determined that the Son of Man must die. But what sorrow awaits the one who betrays Him."[9]

All of us began to look at one another around the table. John was sitting next to Jesus so I motioned to him to ask, "Who's He talking about?"[10]

Jesus responded, "It is the one to whom I give the bread I dip in the bowl."[11]

Jesus dipped the bread and gave it to Judas. We all observed it. John and I looked at one another in disbelief, as if to say, "What does Jesus mean? What is Judas going to do?"

Jesus looked at Judas and said, "Hurry and do what you're going to do."[12]

Judas immediately got up from the table and walked out of the room. What was happening? Was Jesus sending him out to attend to some business . . . or was something else going on?

19

A NIGHT UNLIKE ANY OTHER

$\sim$

*A*fter Judas had departed, Jesus took some bread and gave thanks to God for it. Then He broke it in pieces and gave it to us, saying, *"This is My body, which is given for you. Do this in remembrance of Me."*[1]

After supper He took another cup of wine and said, *"This cup is the new covenant between God and His people – an agreement confirmed with My blood, which is poured out as a sacrifice for you. Take this and share it among yourselves. For I will not drink wine again until the Kingdom of God has come."*[2]

Now as I look back, I understand what Jesus meant when He told us to remember His broken body and His shed blood. But at the time, all I knew was my heart was heavy. This had not been like any other Passover meal we had celebrated together. Jesus was pointing us more to what was to come rather than to what had passed.

We sang a song together and then departed for the Mount of Olives. We had stayed at the olive grove called Gethsemane the previous two nights.

As we made our way there once again, some of the apostles struck up a discussion about who was the greatest among us. This wasn't the first time that question had been raised. We all truly believed Jesus was the Messiah, and most of us believed He would soon declare Himself and establish His kingdom. The debate centered around where each of us would stand positionally when that took place. We had all served Him faithfully these past three years. We all had given up homes and careers to follow Jesus. So, where would we rank in His government once He established His kingdom?

The conversation was rekindled in light of Jesus's statement that one of us would betray Him. None of us could imagine one among us being disloyal to Jesus. Then someone mentioned the seating arrangements around the table. Jesus had given Judas the bread dipped in sauce befitting the guest of honor. Jesus then apparently sent him off on an important mission. Perhaps Judas would have the greatest position in the kingdom.

Then Andrew stated I was the more likely choice. "He often speaks on behalf of all of us," Andrew contended. "After all, Jesus renamed him 'the rock.'" Philip brought up the fact that James, John, and I were often chosen by Jesus to accompany Him to places where the rest of them were not invited. "Perhaps the three of them will have the greatest positions," he added.

Jesus heard the argument taking place, and He interrupted it saying, *"In this world the kings and great men lord it over their people, yet they are called 'friends of the people.' But among you it will be different. Those who are the greatest among you should take the lowest rank, and the leader should be like a servant. Who is more important, the one who sits at the table or the one who serves? The one who sits at the table, of course. But not here! For I am among you as One who serves. You have stayed with Me in My time of trial. And just as My Father has granted Me a Kingdom, I now grant you the right to eat and drink at My table in My Kingdom. And you will sit on thrones, judging the twelve tribes of Israel."*[3]

As we continued walking, I quickened my pace to come alongside Jesus. I could tell He was troubled, so I said to Him, *"Lord, I am ready to go to prison with You, and even to die with You."*[(4)] I had said those words to Jesus on more than one occasion, and each time He had looked at me but said nothing. This night, however, was different. This time He responded by telling me I would deny Him three times that very night. I was heartbroken that Jesus believed I could possibly forsake Him after everything I had experienced with Him.

When we arrived at Gethsemane, I still couldn't get His words out of my mind. He told everyone to remain there near the entrance while James, John, and I accompanied Him a little farther. We walked another fifty yards, then Jesus told the three of us to wait while He walked about a stone's throw farther. We knew He was going to talk to His Father.

I looked at the other men to see if Judas Iscariot had rejoined us. He had not. I couldn't help but wonder where he was and what he was up to. I knew Jesus was distressed, and we all knew we should be praying to the Father on His behalf. But we were exhausted, and soon, one by one, we all fell asleep.

A short while later, I woke up to the sounds of a large mob advancing in our direction. Some of the men were carrying torches and lanterns. As my eyes began to focus, I saw some were Roman soldiers and some were temple guards. Others were dressed in priestly robes. Most of them were armed – some with swords and others with clubs.

I turned to look for Jesus. He was now standing over James, John, and me. As I leaped to my feet, I noticed a few members of the throng stayed with the other disciples, but the bulk of the mob was now moving briskly in our direction. It was then I saw Judas leading the group.

He walked right up to Jesus and very loudly exclaimed, *"Rabbi!"*[(5)] and greeted Him with a kiss. Judas acted as if he hadn't seen Jesus in a long time and extended the traditional greeting for a respected teacher and mentor. But the actions of the men who accompanied him were anything but cordial and respectful.

Jesus responded, *"Judas, would you betray the Son of Man with a kiss?"* [6]

Immediately the captain of the guard told the temple guards to take hold of Jesus and arrest Him. When I saw what was happening, I drew my sword. Interestingly enough, I wouldn't have had the sword if Jesus had not reminded me to bring it as we were leaving the upper room.

A man standing nearby looked ready to swing his club at Jesus, so I instinctively struck him with my sword. My blade was true, and the blow sliced off the man's ear.

Before anyone else could react, Jesus shouted, *"No more of this! Put away your sword. Don't you realize that I could ask My Father for thousands of angels to protect us, and He would send them instantly?"* [7]

I watched as Jesus reached out to the man and touched his ear. Immediately, the man's pain was gone. As he felt his ear, he realized Jesus had restored it. Amazed, he dropped his club to the ground and trembled before Jesus.

We all looked at one another. Jesus had just told us not to fight. The size of the mob was overwhelming. I was frightened and in shock by what had just taken place. I never anticipated the religious leaders sending soldiers in the middle of the night to arrest Jesus. In the confusion of the moment, we feared what was going to happen to Him . . . and to us! I am ashamed to admit we all abandoned Jesus and fled in different directions.

20

NOWHERE TO GO

~

*J*ohn and I ran farther up into the Mount of Olives away from Jerusalem. Once it became obvious no one was following us, we stopped to catch our breath. We hid behind some trees so we could see what was happening to Jesus. We didn't dare look each other in the eye – we were too ashamed for running away and leaving Jesus to fend for Himself.

A few minutes later, the mob completely surrounded Jesus and led Him back to the city. John and I followed at a safe distance so we could see where they were taking Him. They walked about a mile to the home of Annas, the former high priest, in the southern part of the city. John said he was surprised they took Jesus to Annas's home and not the home of Caiaphas, the current high priest.

John had spent time in both men's homes while he attended the school of Hillel. He knew them to be powerful and ambitious leaders who would go to great lengths to increase their dominance and wealth. He explained that since Annas was no longer the high priest, he had no legal standing under

Mosaic law for Jesus to be brought before him. But John had a pretty good idea why Jesus was being taken to Annas's home first.

John told me Annas oversaw the financial enterprises profiting from the buying and selling taking place at the temple. When Jesus cleansed the temple for a second time earlier in the week, Annas saw it as a direct attack on himself, his position, his authority, and on his financial livelihood. He obviously was one of the men behind Jesus's arrest.

John decided to risk entering Annas's home so he could witness what was taking place. After he gained entry, he spoke with the servant woman watching at the gate and arranged access for me. I remained in the courtyard while John was inside the house.

I couldn't hear the conversation taking place inside, but I was so distraught over abandoning Jesus, I wouldn't have been able to concentrate anyway. I also knew John would relay it to me later.

I was warming my hands over the fire, along with the household servants and guards, when the servant woman who had granted us entry came over to me. She knew John was a disciple of Jesus and presumed I was as well. She wasn't one of the accusers, she was simply an inquisitive servant. Who better to ask about the Savior than one of His disciples?

So she asked me, *"You're not one of that Man's disciples, are you?"*[1]

But rather than seeing it as an opportunity to tell her about Jesus, in the midst of the chaos and confusion taking place, I denied I was His disciple.

At that moment I saw Jesus in His bindings being led out of the house. Presuming the mob was taking Him elsewhere, I turned and hurriedly walked away. This time I did not walk with John.

It was only a short distance to the home of Caiaphas. John again followed the mob into the house. With all the confusion, no one was watching the entry into the courtyard, so I made my own way to the fire to warm my hands.

I had always been the one who wanted to be close to Jesus wherever we went. But today, I was content to remain at a distance. As I stood by the fire, the servants and guards began to stare at me and talk among themselves. Soon one of them asked me if I was one of Jesus's disciples. He thought he recognized me from one of the times he had seen Jesus teaching at the temple.

It wasn't an accusation; it was an honest inquiry, just like that of the servant woman. But again, I – the one who had always spoken out boldly when others stood silently – was tongue-tied by fear and cowardly shook my head in protest. So they stopped pressing me.

After a few more minutes, another man approached me. He told me he was a relative of the servant whose ear had been cut off when Jesus was arrested. Word of how Jesus had miraculously healed his ear was already spreading far and wide.

I don't know whether this servant's intention was to accuse me or, more likely, to hear an eyewitness account of the healing. *"Didn't I see you out there in the olive grove with Jesus?"*[2] he asked me. But for the third time, I adamantly denied even knowing Jesus!

I immediately remembered Jesus telling me I would deny Him three times before the rooster crowed the next morning. The moment I denied Jesus for the third time, I heard the rooster crow. I ran from the courtyard weeping bitterly.

I cannot begin to explain the guilt and shame I felt. To make matters worse, I was no longer thinking about Jesus and what was being done to

Him, I was fully absorbed in my own pain. As I ran, I didn't know where to go. I couldn't face anyone. I didn't want to be with anyone. I didn't know what to do.

I wanted time to go backward. I wanted to return to those times walking with Jesus by the shore when everything was peaceful and calm. I wanted to sit beside Him and know everything was going to be all right. I wanted to tell Him how sorry I was and seek His forgiveness. But I couldn't.

Suddenly, I had an idea. I would go to the last place I had been with Him and felt secure. I would go to the upper room where we had eaten together. The place where He had washed my feet. I quietly made my way up to the room; no one saw me. Gratefully, the room was empty. The women had obviously cleaned up after our meal, but otherwise everything looked the same.

I walked over to the place I had sat at the table. I turned and looked at the place where Jesus had sat. As I did, I saw Him in my mind's eye getting up to come wash my feet. And once again, I began to weep uncontrollably.

21

SHAME AND ANGUISH

~

*J*esus knew what I would do. He had known the day when He first called me "Peter." Still, He had chosen me to walk with Him as a trusted follower, knowing I would deny Him. Shame and sorrow continued to overwhelm me; I was drowning in remorse. This sensation of drowning was far worse than the day I sank in the storm-tossed sea – because this time I couldn't call out to Jesus to rescue me. My shame wouldn't permit me.

As the hours passed, I sank deeper and deeper into despair. Even though the sun had risen outdoors, I felt surrounded by complete darkness. I didn't know what was happening to Jesus, but I had a pretty good idea. I had denied my Lord! Earlier, in the courtyard when I denied Jesus for the third time, He had seen me. My eyes had met His for a brief moment. His gaze was not accusatory or condemning; rather, it was one of love and forgiveness.

I could not get that image out of my mind. I could not bear His forgiveness. What I had done was unforgiveable. I was not worthy of His forgiveness. I was not worthy of anyone's forgiveness. I would never be able to face the other disciples. I would never be able to face Gabriella or my daughters. How could they ever respect me? I wanted to die. For a while, I even contemplated how I would kill myself. I considered jumping off the roof of the upper room.

But that thought triggered a memory from the day before. Soon after John and I had arrived at the upper room, we met the owner – a man named Yitzhak – and he had told us a most interesting story.

"Three years ago, my son was helping me finish the construction of this upper room. We were setting the final roof tiles when Uriah lost his footing and fell to the street below. I scurried down as fast as I could. Several of my neighbors were already there by his side. My son was not moving, and I could not tell if he was breathing. Thankfully, a neighbor had already run to get the physician.

"I felt so helpless as I stared at my son. All I could do was cry out to Jehovah God to help me. Just as I did, a Man knelt beside me. He appeared to be one of the pilgrims who had traveled to Jerusalem for Passover. He had been passing by when Uriah fell and came over to see if He could help.

"The next thing I knew, He took my son by the hand and said, 'Young man, I say to you, rise!' Immediately, Uriah sat up. He looked at me, then he looked at the stranger. The stranger returned my son's gaze and said, 'Young man, behold your father.' Then He looked at me and said, 'Father, behold your son!'

"The Man rose to His feet and reached down to help Uriah stand. My son said he felt fine and that nothing hurt; it was as if he had never fallen. I looked at him in disbelief. Just a moment earlier he had been lying there crumpled on the street! The neighbors gathered around us stood there with their mouths agape as if to say, 'How can this be?'

"I was still on my knees looking up at the Man when I asked, 'Who are You? And what did You do?'

"'Yitzhak,' He said, 'you cried out to the Father for help. He heard your prayer and your son has been made whole. All so that the Father might be glorified.'

"'Sir,' I replied, 'how is it You know my name, but I don't know Yours? Even so, I know I have You to thank for restoring my son.'

"'Thank the Father for hearing and answering your prayer,' the Man said as He reached down and helped me stand to my feet. Smiling broadly, He added, 'Thank Him for giving you your son once again. And now go, give the boy something to eat.'

"It was only after He had walked away that I learned His name was Jesus. I can never repay Him for what He did for me. I believed my son was dead, but he's alive because of Jesus!"

Uriah, who was standing beside his father, nodded in agreement as Yitzhak told me the story. When the older man finished, Uriah added, "The next day, I was standing outside the temple. A group of men was talking about how Jesus had chased the money changers out of the temple. I heard one of them say, 'Who does this Jesus think He is? Who put Him in charge of the temple?'

"I surprised myself when I spoke up. 'I think God must have put Him in charge!' I then explained what Jesus had done for me the day before. By the time I was done, the men stopped saying bad things about Jesus and walked away."

Even that young boy had demonstrated the courage to speak up for Jesus. But I – supposedly one of His closest followers – had denied Him out of fear. That thought caused me to shed even more tears of grief.

Later that day, my anguish was briefly interrupted by Yitzhak as he entered the room. He had apparently come seeking a place to be alone in the midst of the day's tragic events. I wanted to know what was happening to Jesus, but I couldn't bring myself to ask him. And he did not appear to feel like talking. When he saw me, he turned around and left the room.

No one else came to the room that day. Most of the others had apparently fled to Lazarus's home in Bethany after the arrest, except the few who had stayed with Jesus.

Late that night, John arrived at the upper room. He told me the news I could not bear to hear. Jesus was dead. He recounted all that had happened and said he had been looking for me. The writer of Proverbs talks about a *"friend who sticks closer than a brother."*[1] That night, all throughout the next day and into the following, John was that kind of friend when I so desperately needed one. I sometimes wonder what I might have done if he had not been there. But in retrospect, I know Jesus was ministering His grace to me through John.

‍∽

22

FORGIVEN!

~

*O*n the third day, before the sun had barely risen, Mary Magdalene showed up at the upper room. She was hysterical. With great effort, she explained that she and several other women had gone to the tomb where Jesus's body had been laid. But when they arrived, the stone used to seal the tomb had been rolled away. "Someone has taken His body!" she cried out.

John and I looked at one another and immediately knew we needed to go and investigate. Who had taken His body – and where had they taken it? Or more likely, had the women simply gone to the wrong place? We ran to the tomb, John arriving first since he was younger. But he stopped at the doorway and looked in. I charged past him and ran right into the tomb.

John confirmed that this was the tomb where Jesus's body had been laid. Mary and the other women were not mistaken. But instead of a body, all we saw were linen wrappings neatly rolled up. John looked at me and said, "Simon, do you remember what He said? He told us, '*The Son of Man is going to be betrayed into the hands of His enemies. He will be killed, but three days later He will rise from the dead.*'"[1]

John later told me it was in that moment that he saw and believed. He couldn't yet prove that Jesus had risen, but He believed it with all his heart. I had not yet come to that place. I didn't know what to think. John decided to go see Jesus's mother who was with the others in Bethany. I resolved to return to the upper room. I still couldn't face anyone else, knowing what I had done.

Throughout the hours that followed, I was in even greater turmoil. Had Jesus's body been taken, or had He risen from the grave like He said He would? I had seen Him raise others from the dead on three occasions. I knew He had power over the death of others. But did He have power over His own death? And if He had risen from the dead, how could I ever face Him? I wanted to see Him. I wanted to tell Him I was sorry. I wanted His forgiveness, but my shame left me in doubt as to whether I could accept it. As the hours passed, I continued to wrestle with my guilty conscience.

All at once, I sensed the presence of someone else in the room. I turned to look, thinking it might be Yitzhak again or perhaps Mary Magdalene. But instead, I was looking into the face of Jesus . . . standing right there before me! He hadn't walked into the room; He had just appeared! "Peace be with you, Peter," He said.

Hearing His voice, I began to weep uncontrollably. I didn't know what to do. Part of me wanted to run and hide because of my shame. But another part wanted to wrap my arms around Him. As I struggled with what to do, I discovered my legs could not move.

Jesus stepped toward me and embraced me – and He didn't let go. I have no idea how long we stood there with His arms wrapped around me. I kept saying, "Jesus, I am so sorry!" And He lovingly responded, "I know you are, Peter. I forgive you."

Jesus knew my denial of Him was now well-known among the other disciples. He knew He would need to correct me and restore me in front of the others. He would do so when the time was right. But at that moment, He knew my broken heart and spirit needed to be healed. Since the first day I met Him, I had known I was a sinner unworthy of His forgiveness. But standing there, with the memories of my denial so fresh in my mind, I was overwhelmed by His mercy, His grace, and His love.

I had denied Him . . . and yet here He was embracing me. I had abandoned Him . . . and yet here He was forgiving me. I had sinned against Him . . . and yet here He was standing before me as my Passover Lamb – having shed His own blood for the forgiveness of my sins.

I knew right then my journey with Him would never be over. I would follow Him to my death. He had extended His grace, His mercy, His love, and His forgiveness to me a sinner, even when I denied Him. And I knew, by His grace, I would never again deny Him.

I wanted that moment to last forever. I wanted to remain in His embrace. But He told me it was time for Him to go. It reminded me of the day we had been with Him on Mount Tabor. James, John, and I hadn't wanted to leave that place, but Jesus had told us it was time to go back down the mountain.

He told me to gather the others and for us to assemble in the upper room. He would appear before all of us later that evening. Just before He left me, He said, "Remember, Peter, I have forgiven you, now you must forgive yourself. And what I have forgiven, I have forgotten. Do not dredge up sins from the past. They are forgiven, forgotten, and covered by My blood."

That night, Jesus appeared to all of us except Thomas. By the time we had come together everyone had heard the testimonies of Mary Magdalene and the other women, John, Clopas, and me. We had all borne witness to the reality that Jesus had risen. There was an excitement in the room that was only eclipsed when He suddenly appeared in the midst of us.

I couldn't imagine why Thomas was absent. The others told me he was still in Bethany at the home of Lazarus – but he had isolated himself from everyone. The next morning, I set out to find my brother-in-law. After much effort, I located him in Lazarus's vineyard. As soon as I saw him, I knew what the problem was. He was wallowing in his shame and self-pity.

"I abandoned Jesus!" Thomas cried out. "I ran in fear. My actions were no better than those of Judas Iscariot. I may not have led the soldiers to Him, but I ran away and left Him to fend for Himself."

"We all did," I replied. "And I denied Him – three times. I know exactly how you feel. But Jesus has forgiven me. He's forgiven us all. Do not hide here in the vineyard. Jesus is alive! Accept His forgiveness."

But Thomas's reply told me he wasn't yet ready to receive what I was saying. *"I won't believe it unless I see the nail wounds in His hands, put my fingers into them, and place my hand into the wound in His side."*[(2)]

∾

23

"FEED MY SHEEP"

~

We all remained in Judea for one more week. Thomas was with us when Jesus again appeared in our midst in the upper room. Jesus rebuked Thomas for his lack of faith, but in reality, it was a reminder for us all. The world may say that "seeing is believing," but in the kingdom of God "believing is seeing." I can tell you firsthand I never saw my brother-in-law forget that lesson again – and neither did I.

That night Jesus told us to make our way to Capernaum and wait for Him there. It gave many of us an opportunity to see our families. After we had been there for a day, I decided we needed to go fishing. We had no idea when Jesus would appear to us, so I enlisted the other fishermen in our group to join me – Andrew, Philip, Bartholomew, the brothers James and John, and Thomas. We fished together each night, then rested throughout the day. The rest of our group slept each night and found other ways to pass the time in the village each day.

One morning, we had been out on the sea all night with no success. Suddenly, a Man called to us from the shore and told us to throw out our net on the righthand side of the boat one more time. Even though we didn't have any idea who He was, something told us to obey. As we did, the fish struck the net, just like they had that day in Bethsaida when Jesus told me to do the same thing. In an instant, we all realized who the Man was, prompting John to exclaim, *"It's the Lord!"*[1]

I jumped into the water and made my way to Jesus as fast as I could. He didn't seem to mind when I embraced him in my wet clothing. The other six finished drawing the net filled with fish before returning to shore. Jesus was already cooking bread and fish over a charcoal fire. He told us to bring some of the fish we had caught and add it to the rest. He was preparing breakfast for us. Soon, those who had not been fishing were also gathered there with Him around the fire.

Jesus had always been preparing us to go out into the world and share His Gospel message, making disciples who would then make other disciples. He even used breakfast that morning to illustrate the point. We were like the fish He had already prepared on the fire. He had called us and taught us, but now there would be others added as He worked through us – just like the fish we now added to the fire. He would show us where to cast the net; we would pull it in.

After breakfast, Jesus asked, "Peter, *do you love Me more than these?*[2] Do you love Me above all others? Do you love Me in a way that causes your love for everyone else to pale in comparison?"

Jesus's questions caught me off guard. I hastily replied, "Of course, I love You, Jesus. How could You think otherwise?"

But then Jesus asked me a second time. This time my response was more passionate, wanting to leave no doubt of my love for Him. But when Jesus asked me a third time, I was deeply wounded by the question.

"Lord, You know everything. You know that I love You,"[3] I replied.

I wanted to assure Jesus I loved Him with all of my heart, soul, and mind. But why did He keep asking me the same question? And then it dawned on me – each of these men knew I had denied Jesus three times on the night of His arrest. Though Jesus had already forgiven me, He was now restoring me to my position of leadership in the presence of the other apostles.

This conversation was for everyone else's benefit. I was confessing my love, and Jesus was confirming His calling on my life to be "the rock." He was asking me to confirm my love once for each time I had denied Him.

In response to each of my answers, Jesus replied: *"Feed My lambs," "Take care of My sheep,"* and *"Feed My sheep."* [4] Jesus was not only publicly restoring me to my apostleship and leadership, He was reminding all of us we were more than just fishers of men, we were also to be shepherds of His sheep – caring for them, protecting them, and nurturing them.

Then He told us we each had a path He had laid out for us to follow. We were to keep *our eyes on Jesus, on whom our faith depends from start to finish.* [5] He cautioned us not to be distracted by people or events around us. We were to persevere to the finish.

Jesus lingered that day and spent time with each one of the other disciples personally, just as He had done with me. He invited each man to walk with Him along the shore. He reminded us that we belonged to Him – and all who are His belong to the Father.

"I am preparing to leave you," He said, "but I will send My Spirit to empower you, guide you, and direct you in all truth. For a time, I will not be with you physically, but I will never leave you nor forsake you. Nurture My sheep in the way they should go as they follow Me and obey My commands. Trust Me and follow Me in all that I have shown you."

Later that evening, Jesus departed. A short while later, 120 of us gathered on the Mount of Olives, just as He had instructed. It had been forty days since He had risen from the grave. As we watched, He was taken up into the sky.

All of a sudden, we became aware of two strangers clothed in white robes standing in our midst. They said, *"Men of Galilee, why are you standing here staring at the sky? Jesus has been taken away from you into heaven. And someday, just as you saw Him go, He will return!"* [6]

24

THE ROCK

~

$\mathcal{W}$e walked the half mile back to Jerusalem and went to the upper room. Yitzhak, who had watched with us as Jesus ascended, told me we could use the room for as long as we needed. We, and he, could think of no place more appropriate to wait for the Holy Spirit to come upon us. If the walls of that room could talk . . . oh, what a story they would tell!

During the days that followed, we prayed and reminded one another of what we had seen Jesus do and what He had taught us. At one point, Thomas reminded us that on the night of His betrayal, Jesus had told us when He returns, we would sit on thrones, judging the twelve tribes of Israel.

We all believed we needed to be prepared for Jesus's return. That meant there needed to be twelve apostles! I stood up and addressed everyone. *"Brothers, the Scriptures had to be fulfilled concerning Judas, who guided those who arrested Jesus, as was predicted long ago by the Holy Spirit, speaking through King David. It was written in the book of Psalms, 'Let someone else take his position.'* [1]

"So now we must choose a replacement for Judas from among the men who were with us the entire time we were traveling with the Lord Jesus – from the time He was baptized by John until the day He was taken from us. Whoever is chosen will join us as a witness of Jesus's resurrection."[(2)]

There were a few men who met that qualification, but the names of Justus and Matthias quickly rose to the top of our list for consideration. Both men were well respected, full of faith and wisdom.

We all prayed, *"O Lord, You know every heart. Show us which of these men You have chosen as an apostle to replace Judas in this ministry."*[(3)]

John reminded us that in the Book of Proverbs it says, *"the lot is cast into the lap, but its every decision is from the Lord."*[(4)] So, the eleven of us proceeded to cast our lots, and Matthias was selected to be an apostle.

Several days later, on the day of Pentecost, we were suddenly interrupted by the sound of a mighty windstorm as it filled the room. Then, what looked like flames of fire appeared and settled upon each one of us. We knew we had just been filled with the Holy Spirit. Each one of us began speaking in different languages we had no prior ability to speak.

Yitzhak's son, Uriah, came running into the room a short time later. "There is a crowd of Jews from all nations gathering outside," he shouted. "They heard the sound of the wind and are now hearing the words you are speaking – each one in his own language. They are beside themselves with wonder. They are asking what is happening? Some are wondering if you are all drunk!"

The other apostles and I walked out into their midst. The people crowded around us and began to say, *"How can this be? You men are all from Galilee, and yet we hear you speaking in our own native languages! Here we are – Parthi-*

ans, Medes, Elamites, people from Mesopotamia, Judea, Cappadocia, Pontus, the province of Asia, Phrygia, Pamphylia, Egypt, and the areas of Libya around Cyrene, visitors from Rome, Cretans, and Arabs. And we all hear you speaking in our own languages about the wonderful things God has done! What can this mean?"[5]

I thought of the account in Genesis about the tower of Babel.[6] God had caused the people to speak in many languages to prevent them from building a monument to their own greatness. But on this day, the Lord had permitted us – through the power and presence of His Holy Spirit – to speak in many languages so the people might simultaneously know the greatness of God. He, who had created the languages to bring confusion, was now using them to bring clarity and declare His glory.

The other apostles and I looked at one another. How were we to respond to these people? If Jesus were here, He would know exactly what to say. He would quote the Scriptures and point them to the Father. But Jesus wasn't here. What had He told us? That we were to be His witnesses. And He would send His Spirit to enable us to do so. The Spirit had come. He had given us all we needed.

Right then, His words echoed in my mind: *"You are Peter. . . and upon this rock I will build My church, and all the power of hell will not prevail against it."*[7] Jesus had seen me for who I would become through the power of His Holy Spirit. He had always called me Peter, but in my mind, I had always been the same old Simon – until now. Instantly, I knew I was no longer Simon the fisherman, I was Peter the rock. Not as a result of anything I had done, but because that is who He had transformed me to be. He would give me the words to speak!

I stepped forward and declared, *"Listen carefully, all of you, fellow Jews and residents of Jerusalem! Make no mistake about this. These people are not drunk, as some of you are assuming. Nine o'clock in the morning is much too early for that. No, what you see was predicted long ago by the prophet Joel:* [8]

'In the last days,' God says,
'I will pour out My Spirit upon all people.
Your sons and daughters will prophesy.
Your young men will see visions,
and your old men will dream dreams.
In those days I will pour out My Spirit
even on My servants – men and women alike –
and they will prophesy.
And I will cause wonders in the heavens above
and signs on the earth below –
blood and fire and clouds of smoke.
The sun will become dark,
and the moon will turn blood red
before that great and glorious day of the Lord arrives.
But everyone who calls on the name of the Lord
will be saved.'"[9]

"People of Israel, listen! God publicly endorsed Jesus the Nazarene by doing powerful miracles, wonders, and signs through Him, as you well know. But God knew what would happen, and His prearranged plan was carried out when Jesus was betrayed. With the help of lawless Gentiles, you nailed Him to a cross and killed Him. But God released Him from the horrors of death and raised Him back to life, for death could not keep Him in its grip.[10]

"God raised Jesus from the dead, and we are all witnesses of this. Now He is exalted to the place of highest honor in heaven, at God's right hand. And the Father, as He had promised, gave Him the Holy Spirit to pour out upon us, just as you see and hear today.[11]

"So let everyone in Israel know for certain that God has made this Jesus, whom you crucified, to be both Lord and Messiah!"[12]

The words the Spirit had spoken through me pierced their hearts, and they cried out, "Brothers, what should we do?"[13]

I replied, *"Repent of your sins and turn to God, and be baptized in the name of Jesus Christ for the forgiveness of your sins. Then you will receive the gift of the Holy Spirit."*[14]

About 3,000 believed and were baptized that day. I couldn't help but think of the times Jesus had told me to cast out the net. He had done so again that day and great was the harvest!

25

NO VALID OBJECTIONS

~

*S*oon after Pentecost, I received a message from Gabriella. I needed to come home to finalize a proposed marriage contract for our oldest daughter, Sarah.

Soon after I departed from Bethsaida to travel with Jesus, and Gabriella and the girls had moved to Capernaum to live, we had become acquainted with a young man named Asher. He was the younger brother of Jairus the rabbi and a skilled carpenter like their father. Though he was almost ten years older than Sarah, it became increasingly apparent the two of them were interested in one another – or so Gabriella advised me.

When I had last been in Capernaum, Gabriella had reminded me that Sarah's sixteenth birthday was approaching. "You realize she will soon be the same age I was when you and I became husband and wife," she said.

"Yes, but he is much too old for her!" I replied.

"Perhaps," Gabriella responded with a smile, "but no older than you were when we married. He is a good man, and he will be a good husband to your daughter. If your only objection is his age, I would say you don't truly have an objection!"

Knowing Gabriella was not going to be put off by me, I had agreed to grant my permission and allow him to finalize his marriage proposal when I next returned home. But much had occurred since that day.

When I received Gabriella's message to come home, I was reluctant to leave Jerusalem and return to Capernaum. In light of all we had experienced since the day of Pentecost, I believed I needed to remain in Jerusalem to preach the Gospel and nurture the many new believers coming to faith. My first thought was that the work would suffer if I were away.

But then I sensed His Holy Spirit reminding me that it wasn't my work, it was His. He was the One bringing the increase, and He was quite capable of doing so without me. He also reminded me that He had called me to be a father.

All of Jesus's half-brothers had come to believe in Him the night of His resurrection. James and Jude in particular had demonstrated a deep faith and understanding of Jesus's teachings. I knew that they, along with the other apostles, were more than capable of continuing the work in my absence.

So I traveled to Capernaum for a three-month stay. The marriage contract was finalized, and we celebrated the union of Asher and Sarah. I was also able to teach in the synagogue there about the resurrection of Jesus and the sending of His Holy Spirit. Jairus, his family, and all of my family were among the first I baptized in Capernaum.

Many of the men who lived in that region had been in Jerusalem for Passover when Jesus was crucified. And most had heard that Jesus had risen from the dead. But few, if any, had remained through the day of Pentecost. So people flocked from throughout the region to hear the Good News.

I was so glad when Nicodemus and his wife, Tali, returned home to Capernaum. They had been with us the day Jesus ascended into heaven, and they had been in the upper room when the Holy Spirit came upon all of us. I was confident that they, together with Jairus and the growing number of believers in Capernaum, would continue the work in Galilee under the power of the Holy Spirit.

My three-month visit passed quickly, and it was time for me to travel back to Jerusalem. "I do not know when I will be able to return," I told my wife. "I know," Gabriella replied, "so we will trust the Lord to bring you back in His time." Then she added with a smile, "But don't forget, Iscah will be sixteen in three years – so you have another daughter to marry off!"

When I arrived back in Jerusalem, I was overjoyed to hear the reports of how the Spirit of God was drawing people to Himself. John and the others were equally delighted to hear about what was taking place in Galilee. The next day, John and I went to the temple to take part in the three o'clock prayer service. A lame man was being carried inside. As we passed by him, he asked us for money.

We stopped, looked at him, and I said, "*Look at us!*"[1] He turned and stared at us. "*I don't have any silver or gold for you,*" I said, "*but I'll give you what I have. In the name of Jesus Christ the Nazarene, get up and walk!*"[2] The man didn't really know who we were, but he knew who Jesus was. And he knew Jesus had healed the lame. When I reached out and took his hand, he immediately jumped up. He stood, walked, then leaped as he praised God. He knew he had been healed by Jesus.

I thought back to a conversation we all once had with Jesus. One of the disciples had asked Him, *"Why was this man born blind?"*[3] Jesus had replied, *"This happened so the power of God could be seen in him."*[4] The same was true of this man who was born lame. He had been born lame so the people would see that same power of God.

As we continued teaching the Good News to those surrounding us, the leading priests, the captain of the temple guard, and several Sadducees came over and interrupted us. "How can you claim there is a resurrection of the dead? You are speaking blasphemy! And you are attributing it to the Man called Jesus who Himself was crucified for speaking such things. Guards, arrest these men!"

After spending the evening in jail, John and I were brought before the high priest, Caiaphas, and the council of all the rulers and elders. *"By what power, or in whose name, have you done this?"*[5] one of the leaders asked.

"Are we being questioned because we've done a good deed for a crippled man?" I inquired. *"Do you want to know how he was healed?"*[6] I told them the man had been healed in the name and power of Jesus – the very One they had crucified, but whom God had raised from the dead.

It would be the first of two times John and I were brought before the council. Each time the Holy Spirit enabled us to proclaim the truth boldly. On this first occasion, we were told to never speak or teach about Jesus again. But we replied, "Do you think God wants us to obey you rather than Him? *We cannot stop telling about the wonderful things we have seen and heard!"*[7] They threatened us and let us go.

On the second occasion, they arrested the other apostles with us and put us all in jail. But to our amazement, an angel of the Lord came to us in the middle of the night and set us free. At daybreak, we returned to the temple to teach. Imagine the surprise of the religious leaders when we were discovered in the courtyard teaching – and not in the jail! That time, they chose to have us all flogged. But our reaction was much different from what they had anticipated. We left the council rejoicing that God had counted us worthy to suffer dishonor for the name of Jesus.

26

THE CHURCH SCATTERED

~

"*W*ho is that man?" I asked, as I turned to John.

"His name is Saul," John replied.

The other apostles and I were taking turns teaching the crowd in Solomon's Porch on the eastern side of the temple that morning. It had been a while since the religious leaders had last threatened us. The crowds continued to increase and the number of believers was growing as we came to the temple each day to teach. This man, Saul, had caught my eye as he made his way toward John. He was a short man and dressed like one of the religious leaders – though I had never seen him before.

"Saul and I studied together under Rabbi Gamaliel," John continued. "He came to rebuke me for teaching the people about Jesus. He insists Jesus is dead, and we have all been deceived. No matter what I said to him, he would not believe it. Saul is a zealous man who aspires to be a member of the high council one day. He concluded our conversation by telling me to watch out. 'If you all continue like this, you too will die – just like your

Teacher,' he said, before we parted ways." I sensed we would be hearing more about this man. Unfortunately, I was right.

The other apostles and I soon realized we must appoint a group of men to serve the growing needs of the believers, particularly the widows. We knew we must concentrate on preaching and teaching the Word of God. We fasted and prayed, and the Spirit of God led us to select seven men to attend to those other needs.

One of the seven was Stephanos, a Hellenistic Jew. He was a man full of God's grace and power. One day, a handful of men under the direction of Saul began to debate Stephanos in the streets. Ultimately, they accused him of blasphemy and brought him before the high council. Though the council had been reluctant to harm the apostles, they apparently had no such hesitancy about harming other believers. As a result, the men, under the watchful eye of Saul, had taken Stephanos to an area just outside the Damascus Gate and stoned him to death.

Soon those types of acts against believers began to occur frequently. Parmenas, another one of the seven, was the next brother to be targeted. It quickly became obvious that the seven men we had chosen to serve were at the top of the list to be tortured. We began to see fewer people gathering to hear our teaching. People were fearful they too would be targeted. Many believers began to scatter to other places.

But as we prayed, we were reminded from the Book of Genesis that what man intends for harm, God intends for good. As the believers were fleeing Jerusalem, the Good News was being carried to other regions and cities. Just before He had ascended into heaven, Jesus told us, *"When the Holy Spirit has come upon you, you will receive power and will tell people about Me everywhere – in Jerusalem, throughout Judea, in Samaria, and to the ends of the earth."*[1]

Unwittingly, the religious leaders were now being used by God to scatter His church, and the Good News, throughout Judea, Samaria, and to the ends of the earth. We soon received word that Philip, another one of the seven, had gone to Samaria. The people there were accepting God's message in great numbers. The other apostles and leaders of the church in Jerusalem decided John and I should go to Samaria to witness what was happening and encourage new believers.

Along the way, we stopped in many Samaritan villages to preach the Good News. Jesus's words were being fulfilled. In the weeks and months that followed, the Spirit of the Lord led me to the town of Lydda – about twenty miles northwest of Jerusalem. I went to visit the church started by residents who had been in Jerusalem at Pentecost nine years earlier.

While in Lydda, I saw a man lying in his bed on the side of the road. His name was Aeneas, and he had been paralyzed for eight years. He had heard of the healing miracles of Jesus but had resigned himself to being bedridden for the rest of his life.

As I looked down at him, the Spirit of God prompted me to say, *"Aeneas, Jesus Christ heals you! Get up, and roll up your sleeping mat!"*[2] Instantly, Aeneas was healed! The whole town saw him walking around. I told him, "Jesus may be out of sight, but He sure isn't gone. Believe on Him and follow Him." The word of his healing quickly spread, and everyone in Lydda and the nearby village of Sharon turned to the Lord. But it didn't stop there – it spread another ten miles toward the coast to the city of Joppa.

Before she became ill and died, a believer named Tabitha had an active ministry as a couturier to the widows of Joppa. Her body was being prepared for burial when believers in the city sent two men to fetch me. The entire region knew Jesus had raised Lazarus from the dead. Now they had heard how He healed Aeneas through me, and they believed Jesus could still raise the dead.

When we arrived in Joppa, the men took me upstairs where Tabitha's body was lying. The room was filled with widows who were weeping and wail-

ing. I was instantly reminded of the day I had accompanied Jesus to
Jairus's home to heal his daughter, Ilana. Jesus had sensed the faithlessness
of those gathered and told them to leave the home. His Spirit prompted
me to do the same.

"Lord, I know You are able to raise this woman from the dead, just as you
did Ilana and Lazarus," I prayed. "Would you now raise this woman from
the dead so the people of this town might turn to You?"

I turned to the body and said, *"Get up, Tabitha!"*[3] Instantly her eyes
opened, and she sat up. The news raced through the town, and many
believed in the Lord. I remained there for a number of weeks, preaching
and teaching the Good News to the Jews.

This was the only instance Jesus worked through me to raise someone
from the dead. He didn't call me to an itinerant ministry of raising the
dead to life; He called me to follow Him and make disciples. That is what I
would continue to do.

≈

27

LED BY THE SPIRIT

~

*W*hile in Joppa, I stayed in the home of Simon the leatherworker who lived near the seashore. He was one of the men who had come to Lydda to fetch me. He also was one of the first people to confess Jesus as Lord after Tabitha was raised from the dead. I was grateful for his hospitality as well as the opportunity to spend more time discipling him in his newfound faith.

Each evening, well into the night, I taught about Jesus to an increasing number of Jews gathered outside Tabitha's home. During the daylight hours, I rested and prayed at Simon's home. Most often, I would go up to the flat roof to pray. The gentle breeze blowing from the sea minimized the unpleasant odors emanating from Simon's tannery.

Around noon one day, I fell into a trance while up on the roof. I looked up and saw the sky open, and something like a large sheet was let down by its four corners. In the sheet were all sorts of animals, reptiles, and birds. Then I heard the voice of my Lord call out to me saying, *"Get up, Peter; kill and eat them."*[1]

I immediately responded, *"No, Lord – I have never in all my life eaten anything that our Jewish laws have declared impure and unclean."*[2]

But the voice spoke again. *"If God says something is acceptable, don't say it isn't."*[3]

The same vision repeated three more times until the sheet was quickly pulled up into heaven. I was perplexed. What could the vision mean? As I thought about it, I was reminded of the night Jesus washed my feet. I had responded to Him in the same manner, *"No, Lord!"*[4] But He had patiently and lovingly taught me – and all of us gathered in that room – how we must serve one another. I had learned the words "no" and "Lord" could never be used together in response to what Jesus told me to do.

As I continued to puzzle over the vision, the Holy Spirit said to me, *"Three men have come looking for you. Get up, go downstairs, and go with them without hesitation. Don't worry, for I have sent them."*[5]

When I made my way downstairs, three men were, in fact, there waiting for me. So I said, *"I'm the man you are seeking. Why have you come?"*[6]

The three men replied, *"We were sent by Cornelius, a Roman officer. He is a devout and God-fearing man, well respected by all the Jews. A holy angel instructed him to summon you to his house so he can hear your message."*[7]

And so my journey to teach and preach the Good News to the Gentiles began. When I arrived at Cornelius's home in Caesarea Maritima, I told him, "You know it is against our laws for a Jewish man to enter a Gentile home or to associate with you. But God has shown me I should no longer think of anyone as impure or unclean. So I came without objection. Now tell me why you sent for me."[8]

The Holy Spirit fell upon all who heard and received the message I shared that day. Even the Jewish believers who were traveling with me could not deny the work of the Holy Spirit. *"Can anyone object to their being baptized, now that they have received the Holy Spirit just as we did?"*[(9)] I asked. So we baptized them in the name of Jesus Christ.

Thus began a debate in the early church that would continue for many years. Did the Gentiles need to become Jews and follow our laws to become a follower of Jesus? Or does salvation come to all of us through Christ alone? And if so, as Jews, we are not saved by our obedience to laws, and neither are we to place that burden on our Gentile brothers and sisters.

Soon after I returned to Jerusalem, Claudius became the new Roman emperor. He chose not to rule Iudaea through a succession of prefects – as several of his predecessors had done – but rather to return Herodian rule to the province. In so doing, he named Herod Agrippa as his new puppet king.

That shift was significant because the prefects had been instrumental in restraining the religious leaders from persecuting the growing church in Jerusalem. Specifically, the prefects had prevented the leaders from conspiring to kill any of Jesus's apostles for fear of how the people might react. But Herod Agrippa did not share that concern. As a matter of fact, he sought to gain favor with the Jewish leaders by doing just what they wanted.

As a result, Agrippa chose to have my cherished friend and fellow apostle, James, the son of Zebedee, arrested and put to death with a sword. We had all known this day would come. Jesus had told us we would be persecuted and killed for His sake. And we knew that to be absent from the body was to be present with the Lord.

That knowledge, however, did not keep me from grieving the loss of one of my oldest and dearest friends. In many ways, we had been closer than brothers. His brother, John, and I wept together at the news. But my grief was soon interrupted when Agrippa's guards came to arrest me. Apparently, the death of James had so pleased the religious leaders that Agrippa decided to gain even more favor by having me arrested.

My arrest occurred during Passover – the thirteenth such celebration since the crucifixion of our Lord. I was imprisoned under the watchful eye of four squads of four soldiers each. The soldiers told me I was to be publicly tried and executed after the conclusion of Passover.

The night before I was to be placed on trial, I was sleeping soundly, chained between two of my guards while the other two stood guard at the gates. I was awakened by a tap on my side. As I opened my eyes, I saw a bright light radiating in my cell. An angel of the Lord stood before me and said, "*Quick! Get up! Get dressed, put on your sandals, and follow me!*"[(10)]

I got up and followed the angel out of my cell. At first, I thought I was dreaming, but as we passed the guard posts, I found myself walking down the street. The angel disappeared and I found myself near the home of Mary, a fellow believer and the aunt of my friend Barnabas. I knew many believers would be gathered there in prayer.

I knocked at the gate to her home. Her servant girl, Rhoda, called out, "Who's there?" However, when I responded, instead of opening the door for me, she ran back into the house!

Mary and other members of her household soon came and let me in. They were as amazed to see me as I was to see them. I told them what had occurred, and together we gave praise to the Lord.

There was much work to be done among both the Jews and the Gentiles, so I hastily set out on my way. I hadn't stayed long enough to see everyone gathered at Mary's. In the midst of their prayer gathering was another whom God was raising up to make His name known among the Gentiles – one whom I had previously known as Saul.

28

THE LEAST LIKELY

~

*T*here was another man at Mary's home who would ultimately become an important ministry partner with me. Mary's son, John Mark, traveled to Cyprus with his cousin Barnabas and Saul – the one eventually called Paul – on what would become known as Paul's first missionary journey. John Mark and Barnabas later returned to Cyprus. On both journeys, they were used by the Lord to preach the Good News to the Jews and Gentiles across the island.

Nine years after my miraculous escape from the prison in Jerusalem, the Lord brought John Mark across my path once again. This time, I invited him to assist me in Rome. He became an invaluable co-laborer in the work. He even helped me record this story you have been reading.

During our time together, I learned he had been with us in the Garden of Gethsemane the night Jesus was arrested. He was only a teenager at the time, and he had secretly followed us from the upper room to the garden that night. After Jesus was arrested, the mob discovered John Mark hiding in the bushes and tried to grab him. He broke free from their grip, but they held onto his cloak so tightly that he ran off naked into the night. He told me he had never shared that story with anyone because he was ashamed of abandoning Jesus. I reassured him he was not the only one who had deserted Jesus that night.

For a man who spent most of his life on a boat in the Sea of Galilee, I was the least likely to be sent by God to the Roman empire to spread the Good News about Jesus. I am not an educated man, or a wealthy man, or a man of social standing. But during my years of walking with Jesus, He taught me that God deliberately chooses people the world considers foolish in order to confound the wise. He chooses the powerless to shame those who are powerful. And He chooses those despised by the world, those counted as nothing at all, to bring to nothing that which the world mistakenly considers important. In so doing, no one can ever boast in the presence of the Lord.

In the days immediately following Pentecost, when the Holy Spirit had come upon us, the religious leaders had been amazed at the boldness of ordinary men who had no special training – other than the fact we had been with Jesus. They had eventually come to fear us, knowing (by their own admission) that if what we were doing *". . . is of God, you will not be able to stop them. You may even find yourselves fighting against God."* [1]

I have never thought much about the fact I am a resident of the Roman empire – although I am not a Roman citizen. But I have grown acutely aware that just as the prophet Daniel wrote, *"God controls the course of world events; He removes kings and sets up other kings"* [2] He has used the Romans to build highways and trade routes to enable the Good News of Jesus to be carried to the ends of the earth.

And one of those ends is the empire's center of power – Rome itself. The Lord didn't direct me to go to Rome through a vision, like He directed me to Caesarea; rather, He used His still small voice. But, nonetheless, it was unmistakable.

The Lord enabled John Mark and me to preach the Gospel throughout the city and see many come to faith. The church was established in Rome, and in the years that followed God led others to come to the city, such as the apostle Paul, to further the work.

After I left Rome to go to Corinth, John Mark remained in the city to further nurture the new believers and leaders. He also needed to complete a task I had given him. During our time together, I had shared my personal account of the ministry, crucifixion, and resurrection of Jesus over countless hours. John Mark had also spoken with many others in the Jerusalem church when he was there, gathering their recollections of Jesus. I told him there must be a written account of Jesus's story, and I believed he was one of the men the Lord had raised up to record it. It would be the first written account about Jesus – at least of which I was aware.

After my time in Corinth, I returned to Rome, which brings me to this current day. Not long ago, a fire broke out in one of the cook shops situated along the side of the Circus Maximus. It was a windy day, and the fire spread quickly. It took nine days before it could be contained. The fire destroyed a substantial part of the city, leaving many dead and many others homeless. The surviving citizens of Rome became incensed against Emperor Nero. Why had he not led the city to react more quickly to extinguish the flames? There were some who said he had set the fire himself.

He quickly took action to divert the blame from himself to the Christians. He announced we were a threat to the empire. He accused us of being a troublemaking people who followed a leader who had been crucified because of His acts of rebellion. He told the people their city – and the entire empire – needed to be purged of Christians before they destroyed the empire. He sent out troops to arrest followers of Jesus. By then there were Christian brothers in the senate and the military who attempted to reason with him, but he would not listen.

He began gathering up Christians and having them crucified on the streets of Rome as a spectacle for the entire city. He was informed that one of the leaders of the movement, one of Jesus's apostles, was in the city. He sent out his soldiers to find and apprehend me at once.

My fate has already been determined, so I have chosen to write this one last letter to my dear wife:

My dearest Gabriella,

I am mindful that in one of my last conversations with Jesus, He told me, "I tell you the truth, when you were young, you were able to do as you liked; you dressed yourself and went wherever you wanted to go. But when you are old, you will stretch out your hands, and others will dress you and take you where you don't want to go."[3]

He was telling me that one day I, too, would be taken to a cross. That day is now apparently upon me. I am told Emperor Nero has decreed that I am to be crucified without further delay. I have told my executioners that I am unworthy to be crucified in the same manner as my Savior, so I have asked to be hung on the cross upside down.

I do not look at the prospect of my death with fear, because I know I will be reunited with my Lord. He has again called to me to step out of the boat and walk to Him on the water. This time, I will not divert my gaze. I will trust Him and keep my eyes focused solely on Him.

My only regret is that I will not see you and the girls and our grandchildren one last time. We made the decision together that I should follow Jesus as one of His disciples that day on the beach at Bethsaida so many years ago. And you have supported me in that decision every day since.

My visits to Capernaum have been much less frequent than I would have liked. And I am mindful we have spent more time apart than we have together. But I thank our God we will have all of eternity to make up for it.

Until then, continue to give all your worries and cares to God, for He cares for you and the girls even more than I do. [4]

Grace and peace be to you until we are reunited in His presence.

Your loving husband,

Simon

PLEASE HELP ME BY LEAVING A REVIEW!

i would be very grateful if you would leave a review of this book. Your feedback will be helpful to me in my future writing endeavors and will also assist others as they consider picking up a copy of the book.

To leave a review:

Go to: amazon.com/dp/1956866116

Or scan this QR code using your camera on your smartphone:

Thanks for your help!

∽

YOU WILL WANT TO READ ALL OF THE BOOKS IN "THE CALLED" SERIES

Stories of these ordinary men and women called by God to be used in extraordinary ways.

A Carpenter Called Joseph (Book 1)

/ *A Prophet Called Isaiah* (Book 2)

A Teacher Called Nicodemus (Book 3)

A Judge Called Deborah (Book 4)

A Merchant Called Lydia (Book 5)

A Friend Called Enoch (Book 6)

/ *A Fisherman Called Simon* (Book 7)

/ *A Heroine Called Rahab* (Book 8)

/ *A Witness Called Mary* (Book 9) releasing March 24

A Cupbearer Called Nehemiah (Book 10) releasing June 16

IF YOU ENJOYED THIS STORY ABOUT SIMON ...

... you will want to read this novel about the shepherd Shimon

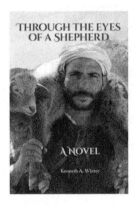

Shimon was a shepherd boy when he first saw the newborn King in a Bethlehem stable. Join him in his journey as he re-encounters the Lamb of God at the Jordan, and follows the Miracle Worker through the wilderness, the Messiah to the cross, and the Risen Savior from the upper room.

Though Shimon is a fictional character, we'll see the pages of the Gospels unfold through his eyes, and **experience a story of redemption – the redemption of a shepherd – and the redemption of each one who chooses to follow the Good Shepherd.**

AVAILABLE IN HARD COVER, PAPERBACK, LARGE PRINT, AND FOR KINDLE, AS WELL AS AN AUDIOBOOK ON AMAZON.

To order your copy:

Go to: amazon.com/dp/1732867097

Or scan this QR code using your camera on your smartphone:

∼

THROUGH THE EYES

... the complete *"THROUGH THE EYES"* SERIES

Experience the truths of Scripture as these stories unfold through the lives and eyes of a shepherd, a spy and a prisoner. Rooted in biblical truth, these fictional novels will enable you to draw beside the storytellers as they worship the Baby in the manger, the Son who took up the cross, the Savior who conquered the grave, the Deliverer who parted the sea and the Eternal God who has always had a mission.

Through the Eyes of a Shepherd (Book 1)

Through the Eyes of a Spy (Book 2)

Through the Eyes of a Prisoner (Book 3)

AVAILABLE IN PAPERBACK, LARGE PRINT, AND FOR KINDLE ON AMAZON.

Scan this QR code using your camera on your smartphone to see the entire series on Amazon:

THE EYEWITNESSES COLLECTION

... you will also want to read "The Eyewitnesses" Collection

The first four books in these collections of short stories chronicle the first person eyewitness accounts of eighty-five men, women and children and their unique relationships with Jesus.

<u>*Little Did We Know*</u> – the advent of Jesus (Book 1)

<u>*Not Too Little To Know*</u> – the advent – ages 8 thru adult (Book 2)

<u>*The One Who Stood Before Us*</u> – the ministry and passion of Jesus (Book 3)

<u>*The Little Ones Who Came*</u> – the ministry and passion – ages 8 thru adult (Book 4)

The Patriarchs — eyewitnesses from the beginning — Adam through Moses tell their stories (Book 5) — releasing in 2023

AVAILABLE IN PAPERBACK, LARGE PRINT, AND FOR KINDLE ON AMAZON.

Scan this QR code using your camera on your smartphone to see the entire collection on Amazon:

∽

LESSONS LEARNED IN THE WILDERNESS

The Lessons Learned In The Wilderness series

A non-fiction series of devotional studies

There are lessons that can only be learned in the wilderness experiences of our lives. As we see throughout the Bible, God is right there leading us each and every step of the way, if we will follow Him. Wherever we are, whatever we are experiencing, He will use it to enable us to experience His Person, witness His power and join Him in His mission.

The Journey Begins (Exodus) – Book 1

The Wandering Years (Numbers and Deuteronomy) – Book 2

Possessing The Promise (Joshua and Judges) – Book 3

Walking With The Master (The Gospels leading up to Palm Sunday) – Book 4

Taking Up The Cross (The Gospels – the passion through ascension) – Book 5

Until He Returns (The Book of Acts) – Book 6

The complete series is also available in two e-book boxsets or two single soft-cover print volumes.

AVAILABLE IN PAPERBACK AND FOR KINDLE ON AMAZON.

Scan this QR code using your camera on your smartphone to see the entire series on Amazon:

———————

For more information, go to:

wildernesslessons.com or kenwinter.org

ALSO AVAILABLE AS AN AUDIOBOOK

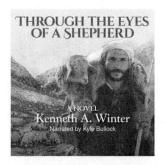

For more information on how you can order your audiobook, go to <u>kenwinter.org/</u><u>audiobooks</u>

SCRIPTURE BIBLIOGRAPHY

∼

Much of the story line of this book is taken from the Gospels according to Matthew, Mark, Luke, and John, as well as The Acts of the Apostles.

Certain fictional events or depictions of those events have been added.

Some of the dialogue in this story are direct quotations from Scripture. Here are the specific references for those quotations:

Preface

(1) Matthew 16:16 (ESV)

(2) John 13:8

(3) James 4:8 (ESV)

Chapter 5

(1) Matthew 3:3, 11

(2) John 1:36

(3) John 1:38

(4) John 1:39

Chapter 6

(1) John 1:42

(2) John 1:43

(3) John 1:45-46

(4) John 1:47-48

(5) John 1:49

(6) John 1:50

Chapter 7

(1) John 2:17

(2) John 2:19

(3) Luke 5:4

(4) Luke 5:5

(5) Luke 5:8

(6) Luke 5:10

Chapter 8

(1) Luke 4:18-19 (referring to Isaiah 61:1-2)

(2) Luke 4:21

(3) Luke 4:34

(4) Luke 4:35

(5) Luke 4:36

(6) Luke 4:38

Chapter 9

[1] Luke 5:20

[2] Luke 5:21

[3] Luke 5:22

[4] Luke 5:27

Chapter 10

[1] Mark 4:35

[2] Mark 4:38

[3] Mark 4:39

[4] Mark 4:40

[5] Mark 4:41

Chapter 11

[1] Mark 5:8

[2] Mark 5:7

[3] Mark 5:9

[4] Mark 5:9

[5] Luke 8:31

[6] Mark 5:12

[7] Matthew 8:32

[8] Mark 5:19

Chapter 12

[1] Luke 9:12

[2] Matthew 14:16

[3] John 6:5

[4] Mark 6:37

[5] Mark 6:38

[6] John 6:9

[7] Matthew 18:3-4

[8] John 6:10

[9] John 6:12

[10] John 6:14

[11] John 6:20

[12] Matthew 14:28

[13] Matthew 14:29

[14] Matthew 14:30

[15] Matthew 14:31

[16] Matthew 14:31

Chapter 13

[1] Mark 8:27

[2] Mark 8:28

[3] Mark 8:29

[4] Matthew 16:16

[5] Matthew 16:17-19

[6] Matthew 17:24

[7] Exodus 30:11-16

[8] Matthew 17:27

Chapter 14

[1] 2 Peter 1:16-17

[2] Mark 5:35

[3] Mark 5:36

(4) Mark 5:39

(5) Mark 5:41

(6) Isaiah 6:5

(7) Luke 9:33

(8) Luke 9:35

(9) Matthew 17:7

(10) Matthew 17:9

Chapter 15

(1) John 11:3

(2) John 11:4

(3) John 11:7

(4) John 11:11

(5) John 11:12

(6) John 11:14

(7) John 11:16

(8) John 11:21-22

(9) John 11:23

(10) John 11:24

(11) John 11:25-26

(12) John 11:27

Chapter 16

(1) John 11:32

(2) John 11:34

(3) John 11:34

(4) John 11:39

(5) John 11:39

(6) John 11:40

(7) John 11:41-42

(8) John 11:43

(9) John 11:44

Chapter 17

(1) John 12:5

(2) Mark 14:6

(3) Matthew 26:11-13

(4) Matthew 21:2-3

(5) Zechariah 9:9

(6) Matthew 21:9

(7) Luke 19:39

(8) Luke 19:40

(9) Matthew 21:10

(10) Matthew 21:11

Chapter 18

(1) Luke 22:10-13

(2) John 13:6

(3) John 13:7

(4) John 13:8

(5) John 13:8

(6) John 13:9

(7) John 13:10

(8) John 13:12-17

(9) Luke 22:21-22

(10) John 13:24

(11) John 13:26

(12) John 13:27

Chapter 19

(1) Luke 22:19

(2) Luke 22:20, 17-18

(3) Luke 22:25-30

(4) Luke 22:33

(5) Mark 14:45

(6) Luke 22:48

(7) Luke 22:51; Matthew 26:52-53

Chapter 20

(1) John 18:17

(2) John 18:26

Chapter 21

(1) Proverbs 18:24

Chapter 22

(1) Mark 9:31

(2) John 20:25

Chapter 23

(1) John 21:7

(2) John 21:15

(3) John 21:17

(4) John 21:15-17

(5) Hebrews 13:20-21 (ESV)

(6) Acts 1:11

Chapter 24

(1) Acts 1:16, 20

(2) Acts 1:21-22

(3) Acts 1:24-25

(4) Proverbs 16:33 (ESV)

(5) Acts 2:7-12

(6) Genesis 11:1-9

(7) Matthew 16:18

(8) Acts 2:14-16

(9) Acts 2:17-21, quoting Joel 2:28-32

(10) Acts 2:22-24

(11) Acts 2:32-33

(12) Acts 2:36

(13) Acts 2:37

(14) Acts 2:38

Chapter 25

(1) Acts 3:4

(2) Acts 3:6

(3) John 9:2

(4) John 9:3

Scripture Bibliography

(5) Acts 4:7

(6) Acts 4:9

(7) Acts 4:19-20

Chapter 26

(1) Acts 1:8

(2) Acts 9:34

(3) Acts 9:40

Chapter 27

(1) Acts 10:13

(2) Acts 10:14

(3) Acts 10:15

(4) John 13:8

(5) Acts 10:19-20

(6) Acts 10:21

(7) Acts 10:22

(8) Acts 10:28-29

(9) Acts 10:47

(10) Acts 12:7-8

Chapter 28

(1) Acts 5:39

(2) Daniel 2:21

(3) John 21:18

(4) 1 Peter 5:7

Unless otherwise indicated, all Scripture quotations are taken from the *Holy Bible*, New Living Translation, copyright © 1996. Used by permission of Tyndale House Publishers, Inc., Wheaton, Illinois 60189. All rights reserved.

Scripture quotations marked (ESV) are taken from *The Holy Bible, English Standard Version*, copyright © 2001 by Crossway, a publishing ministry of Good News Publishers. Used by permission. All rights reserved.

~

LISTING OF CHARACTERS
(ALPHABETICAL ORDER)

~

Many of the characters in this book are real people pulled directly from the pages of Scripture – most notably Jesus! i have not changed any details about a number of those individuals – again, most notably Jesus – except the addition of their interactions with the fictional characters. They are noted below as "UN" (unchanged).

In other instances, fictional details have been added to real people to provide backgrounds about their lives where Scripture is silent. The intent is that you understand these were real people, whose lives were full of the many details that fill our own lives. They are noted as "FB" (fictional background).

In some instances, we are never told the names of certain individuals in the Bible. In those instances, where i have given them a name as well as a fictional background, they are noted as "FN" (fictional name).

Lastly, a number of the characters are purely fictional, added to convey the fictional elements of these stories. They are noted as "FC" (fictional character).

∽

Aeneas – lame man healed in Lydda (UN)
Andrew – son of Jonah, brother of Simon Peter, apostle of Jesus (FB)
Annas – high priest (6 - 15 A.D.) (FB)
Asher – son of Betzalel, brother of Jairus, husband of Sarah (Simon's daughter) (FC)
Avrom – father of Jonah, grandfather of Simon & Andrew (FC)
Barnabas – cousin of John Mark, co-laborer with Saul/ Paul (UN)
Bartholomew (Nathanael) – fisherman, apostle of Jesus (UN)
Caiaphas – high priest (18 - 36 A.D.) (FB)
Chuza – Herod's steward, husband of Joanna (FB)
Clopas – brother of Joseph, earthly uncle of Jesus, father of James (the less) & Thaddeus (FB)
Cornelius – Roman officer in Caesarea Maritima (UN)
Daniel – Old Testament prophet (UN)
Eber – husband of Milcah, father of Gabriella & Thomas (FC)
Elijah – Old Testament prophet (UN)
Emperor Claudius – ruled Roman Empire (41 - 54 A.D.) (UN)
Emperor Nero – ruled Roman Empire (54 - 68 A.D.) (UN)
Enos – the demoniac who was delivered outside of Gergesa (FN)
Gabriella – daughter of Eber, wife of Peter (FN)
Gamaliel – grandson of Hillel (FB)
Herod Agrippa – puppet king who ruled Iudaea (41 - 44 A.D.) (UN)
Hillel – the elder (UN)
Huldah – sister of Zivah, aunt of Simon & Andrew (FC)
Ilana – daughter of Jairus (FN)
Iscah – youngest daughter of Gabriella & Peter (FC)
Ishmael – son of Shebna, father of Salome & Tali (UN)
Jairus – son of Betzalel, rabbi in Capernaum (FB)
James – son of Joseph & Mary, half-brother of Jesus (UN)
James – son of Zebedee, brother of John, apostle of Jesus (FB)
James (the Less) – son of Clopas, cousin of Jesus, apostle of Jesus (FB)
Jesus of Nazareth – the Son of God (UN)
Joanna – wife of Chuza (FB)
Joel – Old Testament prophet (UN)
John – son of Zebedee, brother of James, apostle of Jesus (FB)

John Mark – son of Mary, cousin of Barnabas, colaborer with Barnabas and Simon (FB)

John the baptizer – son of Zechariah & Elizabeth (UN)

Jonah – father of Simon and Andrew (FB)

Jonathan – the boy who gave his sack meal so 5,000 could be fed (FN)

Joseph – husband of Mary, earthly father of Jesus (UN)

Joseph – son of Joseph & Mary, half-brother of Jesus (UN)

Judas Iscariot – the betrayer (FB)

Jude – son of Joseph & Mary, half-brother of Jesus (UN)

Justus – considered, but not chosen, to be twelfth apostle (UN)

Lazarus – brother of Martha & Mary, raised from the dead by Jesus (FB)

Leah – daughter of Nicodemus & Tali, wife of Jairus (FC)

Malchus – servant to Caiaphas (FB)

Martha – sister of Lazarus & Mary (Miriam) (FB)

Mary – mother of Jesus, wife of Joseph (UN)

Mary – mother of John Mark, aunt of Barnabas (UN)

Mary – wife of Clopas, mother of James (the less) & Thaddeus (FB)

Mary (Miriam) – sister of Lazarus & Martha (FB)

Mary Magdalene – one of the women who followed Jesus (FB)

Matthew – apostle of Jesus, former tax collector (UN)

Matthias – chosen by lots to be twelfth apostle (UN)

Milcah – mother of Gabriella & Thomas (Peter's mother-in-law) (FN)

Moses – led Israelites out of Egypt through the wilderness (UN)

Nicodemus – rabbi in Capernaum - pharisee & disciple of Jesus (FB)

Parmenas – chosen by early church to serve widows (UN)

Philip – fisherman, apostle of Jesus (FB)

Philip – chosen by early church to serve widows (UN)

Reuben – son of Nicodemus, took over running of family business from Ishmael (FC)

Rhoda – servant of Mary (mother of John Mark) (UN)

Salome – daughter of Ishmael, wife of Zebedee (FB)

Samuel – son of Chuza & Joanna, healed by Jesus (FN)

Sarah – oldest daughter of Gabriella & Peter (FC)

Saul/ Paul – apostle to the Gentiles, follower of Jesus (FB)

Shebna – brother of Hillel, father of Ishmael (FC)

Shimon – shepherd, disciple of John the baptizer, disciple of Jesus (FC)

Simon – leatherworker in Joppa (UN)

Simon – son of Joseph & Mary, half-brother of Jesus (UN)

Simon (Peter) – son of Jonah, husband of Gabriella, apostle of Jesus (FB)

Simon the zealot – apostle of Jesus (FB)

Stephanos – Hellenistic Jew chosen by early church to serve widows (FB)

Susanna – grieving mother whose son was raised from the dead (FN)

Tabitha – woman raised from the dead in Joppa (UN)

Tali – daughter of Ishmael, wife of Nicodemus (FC)

Thaddeus – son of Clopas, cousin of Jesus, apostle of Jesus (FB)

Thomas – son of Eber, twin brother of Gabriella, apostle of Jesus (FB)

Unnamed man out of whom demons were cast in Capernaum (UN)

Unnamed mother of Zivah – maternal grandmother of Simon & Andrew (FC)

Unnamed relative of Malchus in Caiaphas's courtyard (UN)

Unnamed servant woman in Annas's courtyard (UN)

Unnamed wife of Avrom – paternal grandmother of Simon & Andrew (FC)

Uriah – son of Yitzhak (FC)

Yanis – the paralytic man (FN)

Yitzhak – the tradesman who owned the upper room (FC)

Zebedee – husband of Salome, father of James and John (FB)

Zivah – wife of Jonah, mother of Simon and Andrew (FC)

∾

ACKNOWLEDGMENTS

I do not cease to give thanks for you ....
Ephesians 1:16 (ESV)

… my partner in all things, LaVonne,
for choosing to trust God as we walk with Him in this faith adventure;

… my family,
for your love, support and encouragement always;

… Sheryl,
for enabling me to tell the story in a far better way;

… Scott,
for your artistry and creativity;

… a precious group of friends
who have read an advance copy of this book,
for all of your help, feedback and encouragement;

… and most importantly,
the One who is truly the Author and Finisher of it all
– our Lord and Savior Jesus Christ!

∾

ABOUT THE AUTHOR

Ken Winter is a follower of Jesus, an extremely blessed husband, and a proud father and grandfather – all by the grace of God. His journey with Jesus has led him to serve on the pastoral staffs of two local churches – one in West Palm Beach, Florida and the other in Richmond, Virginia – and as the vice president of mobilization of the IMB, an international missions organization.

Today, Ken continues in that journey as a full-time author, teacher and speaker. You can read his weekly blog posts at kenwinter.blog and listen to his weekly podcast at kenwinter.org/podcast.

And we proclaim Him, admonishing every man and teaching every man with all wisdom, that we may present every man complete in Christ. And for this purpose also I labor, striving according to His power, which mightily works within me.
(Colossians 1:28-29 NASB)

PLEASE JOIN MY READERS' GROUP

Please join my Readers' Group in order to receive updates and information about future releases, etc.

Also, i will send you a free copy of *The Journey Begins* e-book — the first book in the *Lessons Learned In The Wilderness* series. It is yours to keep or share with a friend or family member that you think might benefit from it.

It's completely free to sign up. i value your privacy and will not spam you. Also, you can unsubscribe at any time.

Go to kenwinter.org to subscribe.

Or scan this QR code using your camera on your smartphone:

~

Printed in Great Britain
by Amazon